WORLD STUDIES

STUDENT ACTIVITIES

FOR USE WITH FOURTH EDITION

Dennis Bollinger

bju **press**®

Greenville, South Carolina

NOTE: The fact that materials produced by other publishers may be referred to in this volume does not constitute an endorsement of the content or theological position of materials produced by such publishers. Any references and ancillary materials are listed as an aid to the student or teacher and in an attempt to maintain the accepted academic standards of the publishing industry.

WORLD STUDIES Student Activities
For use with **WORLD STUDIES Fourth Edition**

Dennis Bollinger, PhD

Contributing Writer
Sarah Weaver

Editor
Manda Kalagayan

Cover Design
Drew Fields

Book Design
Dan Van Leeuwen

Page Layout
Jessica Johnson

Project Coordinator
Dan Berger

Permissions
Sharon Belknap
Sylvia Gass
Sarah Gundlach
Carrie Walker

Illustration
Michael Asire
John Cunningham
Preston Gravely Jr.

Photograph Credits
Covers
front LIUSHENGFILM/Shutterstock.com; **back** © iStock.com/tunart

Banners
front matter, chs. 1–2 © iStock.com/alexeys; **chs. 3–6** © iStock.com/Andres Garcia Martin; **chs. 7–11** "The battle of Terheide, 10 august 1653" by Jan Abrahamsz Beerstraaten/Wikipedia/Public Domain; **chs. 12–16** © Marina Ignatova / Fotolia; **chs. 17–20** "Flickr - The U.S. Army - Loading up" by Staff Sgt. Daniel St. Pierre/Wikimedia Commons/Public Domain

All maps from Map Resources

Text acknowledgments appear on-page with text selections.

© 2017 BJU Press
Greenville, South Carolina 29609

First Edition © 1985
Second Edition © 1998, 2000
Third Edition © 2011

Printed in the United States of America

ISBN: 978-1-60682-988-2

15 14 13 12 11 10 9 8 7 6 5

CONTENTS

UNIT III: DOMINANT POWERS IN EUROPE AND ASIA: 1450–1750

UNIT IV: THE REVOLUTIONARY AGE: 1750–1900

Name _____

The Epic of Gilgamesh

An epic is a long poem that records the adventures of a heroic person. *The Epic of Gilgamesh* is one of the oldest stories in the world. It was written more than two thousand years before the birth of Jesus by an ancient people called the Sumerians.

Answer the questions at the end based on the following excerpts from this ancient story. Compare this pagan account with the biblical account in Genesis 6–8 in order to answer the questions.

The Story of the Flood

The hearts of the Great Gods moved them to inflict the Flood.
Their Father Anu uttered the oath (of secrecy),
Valiant Enlil was their Adviser,
Ninurta was their Chamberlain,
Ennugi was their Minister of Canals.
Ea, the Clever Prince. . . was under oath with them
so he repeated their talk to the reed house:
"Reed house, reed house! Wall, wall!
O man of Shuruppak, son of Ubartutu:
Tear down the house and build a boat!
Abandon wealth and seek living beings!
Spurn possessions and keep alive living beings!
Make all living beings go up into the boat.
The boat which you are to build,
its dimensions must measure equal to each other:
its length must correspond to its width."

. . .

The child carried the pitch,
the weak brought whatever else was needed.
On the fifth day I laid out her exterior.
It was a field in area,
its walls were each 10 times 12 cubits in height,
the sides of its top were of equal length, 10 times [12] cubits each.

. . .

Whatever I had I loaded on it:
whatever silver I had I loaded on it,
whatever gold I had I loaded on it.
All the living beings that I had I loaded on it,
I had all my kith and kin go up into the boat,
all the beasts and animals of the field and the crafts-men I had go up.
Shamash had set a stated time:
"In the morning I will let loaves of bread shower down, and in the evening a rain of wheat!
Go inside the boat, seal the entry!"

. . .

[F]orth went Ninurta and made the dikes overflow.
The Anunnaki lifted up the torches,
setting the land ablaze with their flare.
Stunned shock over Adad's deeds overtook the heavens,
and turned to blackness all that had been light.
The . . . land shattered like a . . . pot.
All day long the South Wind blew . . . ,
blowing fast, submerging the mountain in water,
overwhelming the people like an attack.

. . .

The gods were frightened by the Flood,
and retreated, ascending to the heaven of Anu.
The gods were cowering like dogs, crouching by the outer wall.

. . .

Six days and seven nights
came the wind and flood, the storm flattening the land.

. . .

When a seventh day arrived
I sent forth a dove and released it.
The dove went off, but came back to me;
no perch was visible so it circled back to me.
I sent forth a swallow and released it.
The swallow went off, but came back to me;
no perch was visible so it circled back to me.
I sent forth a raven and released it.
The raven went off, and saw the waters slither back.
It eats, it scratches, it bobs, but does not circle back to me.
Then I sent out everything in all directions and sacrificed (a sheep).
I offered incense in front of the mountain-ziggurat.

http://www.ancienttexts.org/library/mesopotamian/gilgamesh/tab11.htm

1. What does Gilgamesh (man of Shuruppak) build to escape the flood? How is this similar to the biblical account? (Gen. 6:14–16) _____

   _____

2. What does Gilgamesh take with him on his vessel? Compare and contrast this with the biblical account (Gen. 6:18–21; 7:13–16). _____

   _____

   _____

3. What are some other differences between the epic's account and the biblical account? _____

   _____

   _____

   _____

   _____

4. What three animals does Gilgamesh send out of his boat to see if the water level has lowered? How is this similar to or different from Noah's actions (Gen. 8:5–12)? _____

   _____

5. What was the first thing Gilgamesh did after he and all the people and animals left his boat? What did Noah do after he left the ark (Gen. 8:16–21)? _____

   _____

Name _____

St. Patrick

Answer the questions at the end based on the following excerpts from St. Patrick's writings.

I am Patrick, a sinner, most unlearned, the least of all the faithful, and utterly despised by many. My father was Calpornius, a deacon son of Potitus, a priest, of the village Bannavem Taburniae; he had a country seat nearby, and there I was taken captive. I was then about sixteen years of age. I did not know the true God. I was taken into captivity to Ireland with many thousands of people—and deservedly so, because we turned away from God, and did not keep His commandments. . . .

But after I came to Ireland—every day I had to tend sheep, and many times a day I prayed—the love of God and His fear came to me more and more, and my faith was strengthened. And my spirit was moved so that in a single day I would say as many as a hundred prayers. . . . [O]ne night I heard in my sleep a voice saying to me: "[I]t is well that you fast, soon you will go to your own country." . . . I went in the strength of God who directed my way to my good, and I feared nothing until I came to that ship. . . . [With this ship, I returned home.]

Once again, after many years, I fell into captivity. On that first night I stayed with them. I heard a divine message saying to me: "Two months will you be with them." . . . And again after a few years I was in Britain with my people. . . . There I saw in the night the vision of a man, whose name was Victoricus, coming as it were from Ireland, with countless letters. And he gave me one of them, and I read the opening words of the letter, which were: "The voice of the Irish"; and as I read the beginning of the letter I thought that at the same moment I heard their voice—they were those beside the Wood of Voclut, which is near the Western Sea—and thus did they cry out as with one mouth: "We ask thee, boy, come and walk among us once more."

[*Upon returning to Ireland, he described how revival broke out among the Irish people.*]

How did it come to pass in Ireland that those who never had a knowledge of God, but until now always worshipped idols and things impure, have now been made a people of the Lord, and are called sons of God[?]

[*In Patrick's letter to the Roman soldiers at Coroticus, he indicates the full extent of the Irish revivals but shows how social events interrupted evangelistic work.*]

I Patrick, a sinner, unlearned, resident in Ireland, declare myself to be a bishop. . . . With my own hand I have written and composed these words, to be given, delivered, and sent to the soldiers of Coroticus; I do not say, to my fellow citizens, or to fellow citizens of the holy Romans, but to fellow citizens of the demons, because of their evil works. Like our enemies, they live in death, allies of the Scots and the apostate Picts. Dripping with blood, they welter in the blood of innocent Christians, whom I have begotten into the number for God and confirmed in Christ! The day after the newly baptized, anointed with chrism, in white garments—the fragrance was still on their foreheads when they were butchered and slaughtered with the sword by the above-mentioned people—I sent a letter with a holy presbyter whom I had taught from his childhood, clerics accompanying him, asking them to let us have some of the booty, and of the baptized they had made captives. They only jeered at them.

"The Confession of Patrick" and "Letter to Coroticus" from J. M. Holmes. *The Real St. Patrick*. Greenville, SC: Ambassador International, 1997. Used with permission.

1. What happened to Patrick when he was sixteen years old? _____

2. What reason does Patrick give for this event? _____

_____

3. What happened to Patrick while he was in Ireland? _____

4. Why did Patrick return to Ireland? _____

5. According to Patrick's confessions, what was the result of his evangelistic work? _____

_____

6. What happened to many of Patrick's converts in Ireland? _____

7. What two groups does Patrick rebuke? _____

Name _____

Chapter Review

Completion

Underline the term that accurately completes the following statements.

1. The book of (Genesis/Romans) explicitly states that God created the world.

2. Those who were not Greek or Roman in culture were called (barbarians/Franks).

3. God rejected the sacrifice of (Cain/Abel).

4. Genesis 10 contains the (Ten Commandments/Table of Nations).

5. The Romans destroyed (Damascus/Jerusalem) in AD 70.

6. The Flood was (local/universal) in scope.

7. Only (Noah's/David's) family survived the Flood.

8. (Constantine/Nero) blamed the Christians for the fire that destroyed Rome in AD 64.

9. The fall of Babel resulted in the (increase/restraint) of sin.

10. Theodosius I made Christianity a(n) (legal/illegal) religion.

11. The (Coptic/Roman Catholic) Church is the official church of Ethiopia.

12. "Messiah" is the Greek term meaning (Forgiver/Anointed One).

13. Constantine changed the name of (Byzantium/Athens) to New Rome.

Matching

Place the correct letter in the blank.

_B_ 14. God spoke the world into existence.

_D_ 15. God performs everything according to His will.

_E_ 16. The result of Adam's sin

_A_ 17. Agreement between two individuals or groups

_C_ 18. Man is responsible to take care of God's creation.

A. covenant
B. Creation
C. Creation Mandate
D. divine sovereignty
E. Fall

Short Answer

Write the answer on the blank.

19. Why should we treat all humans with respect? _they are made in the image of God_

20. What is the most important turning point in history? _death and ressurection of Christ_

Name _____

The God of Islam

Do Christians and Muslims Worship the Same God?

One of the key verses in the Bible, John 3:16, reveals the heart of God—He loves everyone. Although verses such as Romans 3:23 teach that everyone has sinned and missed the mark of God's standard (His glory), we can also say that God loves sinners. However, the god revealed in the Qur'an is very different from the God of the Bible.

Answer the questions based on the following quotations from the Qur'an.

"God bears no love for the impious and the sinful." (Sura 2:276)

"God does not love the unbelievers." (Sura 3:32)

"God loves not the evil-doers." (Sura 3:57)

"God does not love arrogant and boastful men." (Sura 4:36)

1. What do these statements reveal about the god of Islam? _The god of Islam does not love sinners._

2. What would you say to those who claim that Christians and Muslims worship the same God?
   Our God loves sinners, but the god of Islam does not.

A Peaceful Religion?

There is a controversy today about whether or not Islam is a peaceful religion. While many Muslims are peace-loving people, the question about Islam's intentions must still be answered.

Note the following statements taken from the Qur'an, and answer the questions that follow.

"Fight for the sake of God those that fight against you, but do not attack them first. God does not love aggressors. Slay them wherever you find them. . . . Fight against them until idolatry is no more and God's religion reigns supreme." (Sura 2:190–93)

"Believers, make war on the infidels who dwell around you. Deal firmly with them. Know that God is with the righteous." (Sura 9:123)

The Qur'an has special commands for dealing with those who stray from Islam:

"Prophet, make war on the unbelievers and the hypocrites [former Muslims] and deal rigorously with them. Hell shall be their home: an evil fate." (Sura 9:73)

3. Do these statements support the claims that Islam is a peaceful religion? _No_

4. What do these statements reveal about Islam? _They deal with "unbelievers" using violence_

Name _____

Shiite Versus Sunni

Read the following article, and fill in the blanks from the information provided.

Muhammad died in 632. Abu Bakr, an early follower of Muhammad, used military force to become the first caliph, or leader, of Islam. He expanded the Muslim empire during his brief reign before dying in 634. Islamic leaders then selected Umar, a skilled Muslim general, to serve as the second caliph. Under his leadership, Islamic forces quickly conquered territories to the north and west.

Umar was killed by other Muslims in 644, and Uthmann, another Muslim general, became the third caliph. However, the violence continued, and Uthmann died at the hands of his own troops in 656.

At this time Islam split into two groups. Uthmann's forces declared that Muhammad had intended Ali, Muhammad's cousin, to rule. Thus they rejected the rule of the first three caliphs. They took the title of Shiite ("follower") because they claimed to be the true followers of Muhammad. The Shiites insisted that the right of rule was limited to members of Muhammad's family. They also believed that their leader should retain Muhammad's dual role of political and religious leader. The Shiites called this leader their imam rather than caliph.

The majority of Muslims, however, continued to support the established practice of appointing caliphs. They took the name Sunni ("adherent"). The Sunnis believed that any worthy Muslim could become the ruler of Islam. In addition, they divided leadership between a political leader (caliph) and a local religious leader of a mosque (imam).

Following a civil war, the Sunni position remained the dominant position in the Muslim world (80–90%). Today the Shiites represent only about 10% of the growing Muslim population. These two interpretations of Islam continue to this day, and much Muslim-on-Muslim violence stems from this early division.

Issue	*Shiite*	*Sunni*
Meaning of name	_____ (of Muhammad)	_____ (to the customary practice of appointing caliphs)
Successor to Muhammad	Muhammad's cousin _____	_____ appointed to lead
Potential successors	members of _____ family	_____ Muslim
Political leader	_____ holds political and religious authority	_____
Religious leader		_____
Percentage of Muslims	____%	_____%

Name _____

Background of Islam

If the statement is true, write the word *true* in the blank. If it is false, change the bold word(s) to make the statement true.

Mecca   1. Muhammad was born in **Medina**.

true   2. The flight to Medina is known as the **Hegira**.

five   3. There are **six** pillars of Islam.

polytheistic   4. Muslims think that Christianity is a **monotheistic** religion.

Abbasid   5. The **Umayyad** caliphate defeated the **Abbasid** caliphate.

Umayad

flourished   6. Knowledge **perished** under Islamic rule during Islam's Golden Age.

Greek   7. The Byzantine Empire used **Roman** fire to slow the advance of Islam.

true   8. **Charles Martel** effectively ended the Muslim threat at the Battle of Tours.

true   9. After Muhammad died, branches of Islam fought **Wars of Apostasy**.

Sunni   10. The two major Islamic groups are **caliph** and Shiite.

Name _____

Chapter Review
Completion
Underline the term that accurately completes each of the following statements.

1. Muslims believe that Jesus was a (real/fictional) person.

2. Islam teaches that the (Bible/Qur'an) is the final revelation from God.

3. According to Islam/Muhammad received his visions from (Gabriel/Michael).

4. The Qur'an and the Hadith teach (warfare/dialogue) against those who reject Islam.

5. Islam first spread in the (Iberian/Arabian) Peninsula.

6. The Arabs defeated the (Sassanid/Byzantine) Empire in 637.

7. Islam believes that the (Qur'an/Bible) contains errors and contradictions.

8. The Islamic Golden Age of learning and culture occurred during the (Umayyad/Abbasid) caliphate.

9. Followers of Islam are (allowed/forbidden) to convert to another religion.

10. The Byzantine Empire used (Greek fire/boiling oil) as a secret weapon to defeat Islamic armies.

11. The (Russians/Franks) in Western Europe stopped the spread of Islam in 732.

12. Muslims are required to make a pilgrimage to (Baghdad/Mecca).

13. (*Hegira*/*Caliph*) is derived from the Arabic word for *successor*.

14. (Baghdad/Damascus) was the capital of the Umayyad dynasty.

15. The Ka'bah is located in (Medina/Mecca/Damascus).

Matching
Place the correct letter in the blank.

| A. imam | C. Ka'bah | E. sharia |
| B. jihad | D. Ramadan | |

__C__ 16. Stone building at Mecca

__D__ 17. The holy month to Muslims

__E__ 18. Law developed early in the history of Islam

__B__ 19. "Holy war"

__A__ 20. Leader of the Shiites

Name _____

The Eskimo Creation Narrative

Read the following story, and take note of the similarities and differences between the Eskimo creation story and the Genesis account of Creation.

It was in the time when there were no people on the earth plain. During four days the first man lay coiled up in the pod of a beach-pea. On the fifth day he stretched out his feet and burst the pod, falling to the ground, where he stood up, a full-grown man. He looked about him, and then moved his hands and arms, his neck and legs, and examined himself curiously. Looking back, he saw the pod from which he had fallen, still hanging to the vine, with a hole in the lower end, out of which he had dropped. Then he looked about him again and saw that he was getting farther away from his starting place, and that the ground moved up and down under his feet and seemed very soft. After a while he had an unpleasant feeling in his stomach, and he stooped down to take some water into his mouth from a small pool at his feet. The water ran down into his stomach and he felt better. When he looked up again he saw approaching, with a waving motion, a dark object which came on until just in front of him, when it stopped, and, standing on the ground, looked at him. This was a raven, and, as soon as it stopped, it raised one of its wings, pushed up its beak, like a mask, to the top of its head, and changed at once into a man. Before he raised his mask Raven had stared at the man, and after it was raised he stared more than ever, moving about from side to side to obtain a better view. As last he said: "What are you? Whence did you come? I have never seen anything like you." Then the Raven looked at Man, and was still more surprised to find that this strange new being was so much like himself in shape.

Then he told Man to walk away a few steps, and in astonishment exclaimed again: "Whence did you come? I have never seen anything like you before." To this Man replied: "I came from the pea-pod." And he pointed to the plant from which he came. "Ah!" exclaimed Raven, "I made that vine, but did not know that anything like you would ever come from it. Come with me to the high ground over there; this ground I made later, and it is still soft and thin, but it is thicker and harder there."

In a short time they came to the higher land, which was firm under their feet. Then Raven asked Man if he had eaten anything. The latter answered that he had taken some soft stuff into him at one of the pools. "Ah!" said Raven, "you drank some water. Now wait for me here."

Then he drew down the mask over his face, changing again into a bird, and flew far up into the sky where he disappeared. Man waited where he had been left until the fourth day, when Raven returned, bringing four berries in his claws. Pushing up his mask, Raven became a man again and held out two salmonberries and two heathberries, saying, "Here is what I have made for you to eat. I also wish them to be plentiful over the earth. Now eat them." Man took the berries and placed them in his mouth one after the other and they satisfied his hunger. . . . Raven then led Man to a small creek near by and left him while he went to the water's edge and molded a couple of pieces of clay into the form of a pair of mountain sheep, which he held in his hand, and when they became dry he called Man to show him what he had done. Man thought they were very pretty, and Raven told him to close his eyes. As soon as Man's eyes were closed Raven drew down his mask and waved his wings four times over the images, when they became endowed with life and bounded away as full-grown mountain sheep. . . .

"You will be very lonely by yourself," said Raven. "I will make you a companion." He then went to a spot some distance from where he had made the animals, and, looking now and then at Man, made an image very much like him. Then he fastened a lot of fine water grass on the back of the head for hair, and after the image had dried in his hands, he [waved] his wings over it as before and a beautiful young woman arose and stood beside Man. "There," cried Raven, "is a companion for you," and he led them back to a small knoll near by.

Barbara C. Sproul. *Primal Myths: Creation Myths Around the World.* (New York: Harper & Row Publishers, 1979). 220–22.

Compare Genesis 1–2 with the Eskimo creation narrative. Discuss some of the similarities and differences between the two passages.

Similarities

_____

_____

_____

_____

_____

_____

_____

Differences

_____

_____

_____

_____

_____

_____

_____

Name _____

The Yoruba Creation Narrative

Answer the questions following this excerpt from the Yoruba creation narrative.

Obatala [a lesser god under the main god] lived on, with only his black cat for a companion. He thought, "Surely it would be better if many people were living here." He decided to create people. He dug clay from the ground, and out of the clay he shaped human figures which he then laid out to dry in the sun. He worked without resting. He became tired and thirsty. He said to himself, "There should be palm wine in this place to help a person go on working." So he put aside the making of humans and went to the palm trees to draw their inner fluid, out of which he made palm wine. When it was fermented he drank. He drank for a long while. When he felt everything around him softening he put aside his gourd cup and went back to modeling human figures. But because Obatala had drunk so much wine his fingers grew clumsy, and some of the figures were misshapen. Some had crooked backs or crooked legs, or arms that were too short. Some did not have enough fingers, some were bent instead of being straight. Because of the palm wine inside him, Obatala did not notice these things. And when he had made enough figures to begin the populating of Ife [earth] he called out to Olorun the Sky God [the main god], saying, "I have made human beings to live with me here in Ife, but only you can give them the breath of life." Olorun heard Obatala's request, and he put breath in the clay figures. They were no longer clay, but people of blood, sinews, and flesh. They arose and began to do the things that humans do. They built houses for themselves near Obatala's house, and in this way the place Obatala named Ife became the city of Ife.

But when the effects of the palm wine had worn off Obatala saw that some of the humans he had made were misshapen, and remorse filled his heart. He said: "Never again will I drink palm wine. From this time on I will be the special protector of all humans who have deformed limbs or who have otherwise been created imperfectly." Because of Obatala's pledge, humans who later came to serve him also avoided palm wine, and the lame, the blind and those who had no pigment in their skin invoked his help when they were in need.

Molefi Kete Asante and Abu S. Abarry, eds. *African Intellectual Heritage: A Book of Sources*. (Philadelphia: Temple University Press, 1996). 47.

1. List two similarities between this creation account and that found in the book of Genesis. _____

   _____

   _____

2. List four differences between this account and the Genesis account. _____

   _____

   _____

   _____

   _____

3. In passing down this story, what negative things did the Yoruba admit about their god? (You should be able to find at least three things.) _____

   _____

   _____

Name _____

Fictional Journal Entries

Fill in the blanks with words from the word bank. Words may be used more than once.

~~Muslim~~	animism	camels
Sahara	oral	clan

Journal entry of an African boy

Thanks to the ___Muslim___ traders, I know how to read and write. My ancestors used to pass down history to the next generation through ___oral___ tradition. Our ___clan___ is getting larger. My brother's new wife just came to join our community. Soon my father will be leaving with some of my other brothers on the ___camels___ to travel across the ___Sahara___. I can't wait until I am old enough to go on the journey. All of my friends want to go as well. We used to worship the spirits in the trees when we practiced ___animism___. Now we know that Allah is God, and we are a part of the ___Muslim___ faith. Sometimes I wonder who is right. I wish I could talk to my ancestors about it.

read	oasis	slaves	sandstorm
salt	Sahara	write	camels

Journal entry of a Muslim trader

Another long hot day in the ___Sahara___: it is a good thing that the ___camels___ don't need water till we get to the next ___oasis___. I wish my ___slaves___ were in better shape because they must be ready when we get to the city. The ___sandstorm___ last night blew some of my supplies away. Next time I will not forget to secure everything. We are hoping to get lots of ___salt___ for our gold. It is the best way to preserve our food. We got rid of that scholar. I am more interested in business than teaching people to ___read___ and ___write___. Now it is time for some rest.

Name _____

Africa

Locate the following on the maps and
place each number in the correct blank.

_5_ 1. Ethiopia

_6_ 2. Timbuktu

_1_ 3. Sahara

_2_ 4. Nile River

_4_ 5. Atlantic Ocean

_3_ 6. Indian Ocean

_10_ 7. Mediterranean Sea

_9_ 8. Red Sea

_8_ 9. Savannah

_7_ 10. Sahel

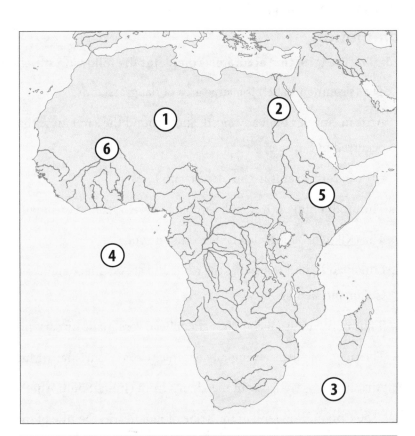

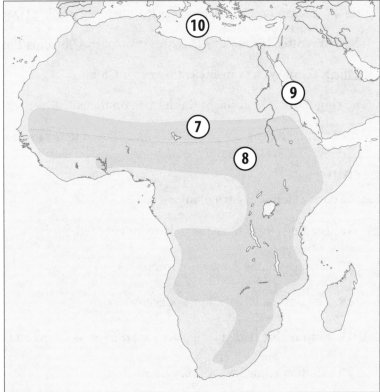

Name _____

Chapter Review

Completion

Underline the term that accurately completes the following statements.

1. The (savannah/Sahel) is a large area of flat grasslands.

2. African empires built advanced cities around the same time that the (Renaissance/Middle Ages) occurred in Europe.

3. Africans grew yams in the (desert/rain forests).

4. The production of (iron/silk) probably developed independently in Africa.

5. The (Kikuyu/Bantu) clan believed in one god.

6. Ethiopian legend states that the cathedral at Aksum contained the (ark of the covenant/Ten Commandments).

7. Some of the unusual churches at Lalibela were made by carving into rock (above/below) ground level.

8. The rulers of Ghana eventually became (Coptic Christians/Muslims) by the eleventh century.

9. African towns traded with merchants from (India/South America).

10. "The Conquering Lion of the Tribe of Judah" was the title of the leader of (Ethiopia/Mali).

11. Ethiopian legend regards Menelik as the offspring of King (David/Solomon).

12. The first written history of Africa was penned by (Muslims/Portuguese).

13. (Cathay/Cambay) was an ancient name for China.

14. The kingdom of (Mali/Kush) was located on the Nile River between Egypt and Ethiopia.

15. Africans forged (iron/copper) into tools and used it as a form of money.

Matching

Place the correct letter in each blank.

__D__ 16. Leading city of the African kingdom of Mali

__B__ 17. Key port in the Zimbabwe empire

__C__ 18. The destination of Coptic pilgrims

__E__ 19. Empire that traded with places as far away as China and India

__A__ 20. Another name for the Ivory Coast

A. Gold Coast
B. Kilwa
C. Lalibela
D. Timbuktu
E. Zimbabwe

Name _____

Asia and Surrounding Countries

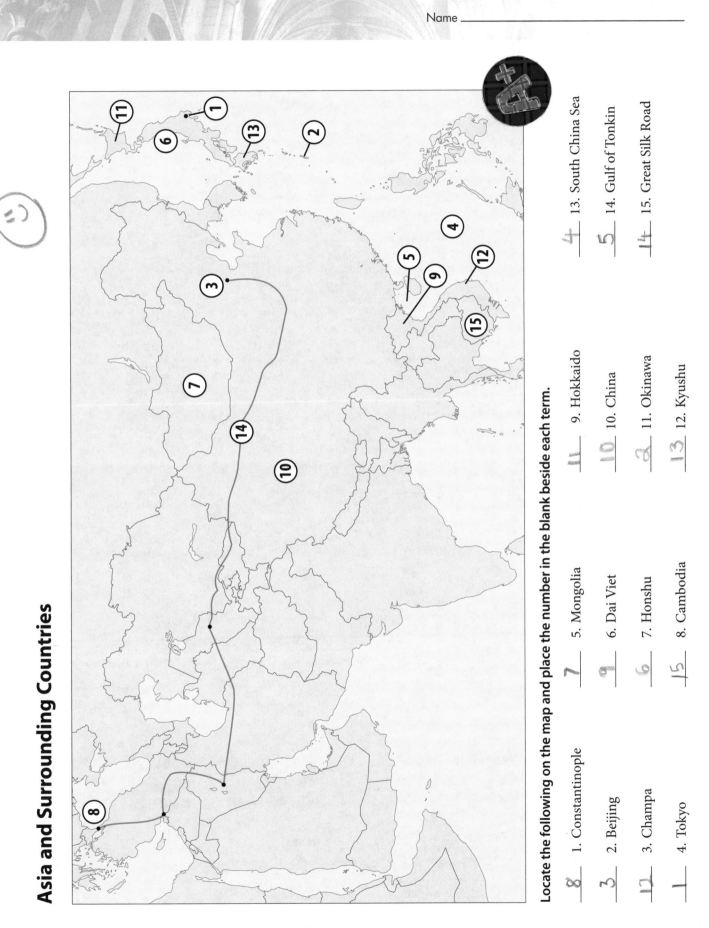

Locate the following on the map and place the number in the blank beside each term.

8	1. Constantinople	**7**	5. Mongolia	**11**	9. Hokkaido	**4**	13. South China Sea
3	2. Beijing	**9**	6. Dai Viet	**10**	10. China	**5**	14. Gulf of Tonkin
12	3. Champa	**6**	7. Honshu	**2**	11. Okinawa	**14**	15. Great Silk Road
1	4. Tokyo	**15**	8. Cambodia	**13**	12. Kyushu		

23

Name _____

Marco Polo's Journals

Answer the questions at the end based on the following excerpts from Marco Polo's writings about these three regions.

[Samarkand] is a noble city, adorned with beautiful gardens, and surrounded by a plain, in which are produced all the fruits that man can desire. The inhabitants, who are partly Christians and partly Mahometans [Muslims], are subject to the dominion of a nephew of the grand khan, with whom, however, he is not upon amicable terms, but on the contrary there is perpetual strife and frequent wars between them. This city lies in the direction of north-west.

. . . .

In this province (of Terduk) was the principal seat of government of the sovereigns styled Prester John, when they ruled over the Tartars of this and the neighbouring countries, and which their successors occupy to the present hour. George, above-mentioned, is the fourth in descent from Prester John, of whose family he is regarded as the head. There are two regions in which they exercise dominion. These in our part of the world are named Gog and Magog, but by the natives Ung and Mongul; in each of which there is a distinct race of people. In Ung they are Gog, and in Mongul they are Tartars. Traveling seven days through this province, in an easterly direction, towards Cathay [China], you pass many towns inhabited by idolaters, as well as by Mahometans and Nestorian Christians. They gain their living by trade and manufactures, weaving, fine-gold tissues, ornamented with mother-of-pearl, named nascici, and silks of different textures and colours, not unlike those of Europe; together with a variety of woollen cloths. These people are all subjects of the grand khan. One of the towns, named Sindichin, is celebrated for the manufacture of all kinds of arms, and every article necessary for the equipment of troops. In the mountainous part of the province there is a place called Idifa, in which is a rich mine of silver, from whence large quantities of that metal are obtained. There are also plenty of birds and beasts.

. . . .

[Kublai Khan] usually resides during three months of the year, namely, December, January, and February, in the great city of Kanbalu, situated towards the north-eastern extremity of the province of Cathay; and here, on the southern side of the new city, is the site of his vast palace, the form and dimensions of which are as follows. In the first place is a square enclosed with a wall and deep ditch; each side of the square being eight miles in length, and having at an equal distance from each extremity an entrance-gate, for the concourse of people resorting thither from all quarters. . . . [T]he bridles, saddles, stirrups, and other furniture serving for the equipment of cavalry, occupy one storehouse; the bows, strings, quivers, arrows, and other articles belonging to archery, occupy another; cuirasses, corselets, and other armour formed of leather, a third storehouse; and so of the rest. Within this walled enclosure there is still another, of great thickness, and its height is full twenty-five feet. The battlements or crenated parapets are all white. This also forms a square four miles in extent, each side being one mile, and it has six gates, disposed like those of the former enclosure. It contains in like manner eight large buildings. . . . The spaces between the one wall and the other are ornamented with many handsome trees, and contain meadows in which are kept various kinds of beasts, such as stags, the animals that yield the musk, roe-bucks, fallow-deer, and others of the same class. Every interval between the walls, not occupied by buildings, is stocked in this manner. The pastures have abundant herbage. . . . The palace contains a number of separate chambers, all highly beautiful, and so admirably disposed that it seems impossible to suggest any improvement to the system of their arrangement. The exterior of the roof is adorned with a variety of colours, red, green, azure, and violet, and the sort of covering is so strong as to last for many years. The glazing of the windows is so well wrought and so delicate as to have the transparency of crystal. In the rear of the body of the palace there are large buildings containing several apartments, where is deposited the private property of the monarch, or his treasure in gold and silver bullion, precious stones, and pearls, and also his vessels of gold and silver plate.

Marco Polo. *The Travels of Marco Polo.* Trans. William Marsden. Ed. William Marsden and Thomas Wright. (Garden City, NY: Doubleday, 1948). 62–63, 96–97, 120–22.

1. What important city did Marco Polo visit which he described as being "surrounded by a plain, in which are produced all the fruits that man can desire"? _____

2. What religious groups did Polo find in this city? _____
_____

3. In what town did Polo find "every article necessary for the equipment of troops"? _____

4. Besides riches, what objects were located at the khan's palace? What characteristics about the Mongols did these objects suggest? _____
_____
_____

5. Using Polo's words, describe Kublai Khan's palace. _____
_____
_____

6. Imagine that you were living in Europe during this time. From reading Polo's accounts, how would you have pictured China? _____
_____
_____
_____

Name _____

Asia

Place the correct answer in each blank.

Japan

B	1.	Unwritten military code
E	2.	Method of suicide
F	3.	Japan's capital beginning in 1192
D	4.	Dominant clan in the 700s
I	5.	Central leader of Japan ("great general")
K	6.	Dominant clan who moved the capital to Tokyo in 1603
C	7.	Social system characterized by loyalty to a local ruler
L	8.	Another name for the city of Edo
M	9.	Established a new line of rulers in 1192
A	10.	Dominant clan starting in 1336 during the second feudal period
G	11.	Japanese warrior
H	12.	Religion that stresses worship of nature and the emperor
J	13.	Transition from local rule to a central ruler
N	14.	Religion that stresses intense mental concentration

A. Ashikaga
B. Bushido
C. feudalism
D. Fujiwara
E. hara-kiri
F. Kamakura
G. samurai
H. Shintoism
I. shogun
J. Taika Reform
K. Tokugawa
L. Tokyo
M. Yoritomo
N. Zen Buddhism

Southeast Asia

_____	15.	Land that forms the western border of the South China Sea
_____	16.	Land influenced by India and China
_____	17.	Empire that developed in Cambodia between the ninth and thirteenth centuries
_____	18.	Central and southern kingdom
_____	19.	Ancient name for Cambodia
_____	20.	Gained control of Champa in 1471

A. Angkor
B. Cambodia
C. Champa
D. Dai Viet
E. Khmer
F. Vietnam

Mongol Invasion of Japan

Answer the questions at the end based on the following excerpt from Marco Polo's writings.

Zipangu [Japan] is an island in the eastern ocean, situated at the distance of about fifteen hundred miles from the main-land, or coast of Manji [China]. It is of considerable size; its inhabitants have fair complexions, are well made, and are civilized in their manners. Their religion is the worship of idols. They are independent of every foreign power, and governed only by their own kings. They have gold in the greatest abundance, its sources being inexhaustible, but as the king does not allow of its being exported, few merchants visit the country, nor is it frequented by much shipping from other parts. To this circumstance we are to attribute the extraordinary richness of the sovereign's palace, according to what we are told by those who have access to the place. The entire roof is covered with a plating of gold, in the same manner as we cover houses, or more properly churches, with lead. The ceilings of the halls are of the same precious metal; many of the apartments have small tables of pure gold, of considerable thickness; and the windows also have golden ornaments. So vast, indeed, are the riches of the palace, that it is impossible to convey an idea of them. In this island there are pearls also, in large quantities, of a red (pink) colour, round in shape, and of great size, equal in value to, or even exceeding that of the white pearls. . . . There are also found there a number of precious stones.

Of so great celebrity was the wealth of this island, that a desire was excited in the breast of the grand khan Kublai, now reigning, to make the conquest of it, and to annex it to his dominions. In order to effect this, he fitted out a numerous fleet, and embarked a large body of troops, under the command of two of his principal officers, one of whom was named Abbacatan, and the other Vonsancin. The expedition sailed from the ports of Zai-tun and Kin-sai, and, crossing the intermediate sea, reached the island in safety; but in consequence of a jealousy that arose between the two commanders, one of whom treated the plans of the other with contempt and resisted the execution of his orders, they were unable to gain possession of any city or fortified place, with the exception of one only, which was carried by assault, the garrison having refused to surrender. . . .

It happened, after some time, that a north wind began to blow with great force, and the ships of the Tartars, which lay near the shore of the island, were driven foul of each other. It was determined thereupon, in a council of the officers on board, that they ought to disengage themselves from the land; and accordingly, as soon as the troops were re-embarked, they stood out to sea. The gale, however, increased to so violent a degree that a number of the vessels foundered. The people belonging to them, by floating upon pieces of the wreck, saved themselves upon an island lying about four miles from the coast of Zipangu. The other ships . . . directed their course homewards, and returned to the grand khan. Those of the Tartars who remained upon the island where they were wrecked, and who amounted to about thirty thousand men, finding themselves left without shipping, abandoned by their leaders, and having neither arms nor provisions, expected nothing less than to become captives or to perish; especially as the island afforded no habitations where they could take shelter and refresh themselves. As soon as the gale ceased and the sea became smooth and calm, the people from the main island of Zipangu came over with a large force, in numerous boats, in order to make prisoners of these shipwrecked Tartars, and having landed, proceeded in search of them, but in a straggling, disorderly manner. The Tartars, on their part, acted with prudent circumspection [awareness, caution], and, being concealed from view by some high land in the centre of the island, whilst the enemy were hurrying in pursuit of them by one road, made a circuit of the coast by another, which brought them to the place where the fleet of boats was at anchor. Finding these all abandoned, but with their colours flying, they instantly seized them and pushing off from the island, stood for the principal city of Zipangu, into which, from the appearance of the colours, they were suffered to enter unmolested. Here they found few of the inhabitants besides women, whom they retained for their own use, and drove out all others. When the king was apprised of what had taken place, he was much afflicted, and immediately gave directions for a strict blockade of the city, which was so effectual that not any person was suffered to enter or to escape from it, during six months that the siege continued. At the expiration of this time, the Tartars, despairing of succour, surrendered upon the condition of their lives being spared. These events took place in the course of the year 12[7]4.

Marco Polo. *The Travels of Marco Polo*. Trans. William Marsden. Ed. William Marsden and Thomas Wright. (Garden City, NY: Doubleday, 1948). 254–57.

1. How did Marco Polo describe Japanese religion? _____

2. How did Polo describe the Japanese in appearance and manners? _____

   _____

3. According to Polo, what did the Japanese have in abundance? _____

4. What can you conclude from the following statement by Polo: "according to what we are told by those who

   have access to the place"? _____

   _____

5. How do you think a European in the Middle Ages would react after reading about Japan? _____

   _____

6. Why did Kublai Khan want to conquer Japan? _____

7. Why were the Tartars [Mongols] forced to surrender? _____

   _____

Name _____

Chapter Review
Completion

Underline the term that accurately completes each of the following statements.

1. A samurai was a (Chinese/<u>Japanese</u>) warrior.

2. The (<s>Shang</s>/Ming) dynasty was the earliest known dynasty in China.

3. (<u>China</u>/Japan) carried on extensive trade with other nations.

4. The (Mongols/<u>Chinese</u>) developed the production of silk.

5. The (merchants/<u>scholars</u>) were highly regarded in China.

6. The Japanese borrowed (Hinduism/<u>Buddhism</u>) from China.

7. The (<u>merchants</u>/scholars) were considered dangerous in China because of their wealth and mobility.

8. Siege warfare was used effectively by the (Japanese/<u>Mongols</u>) in battle.

9. The Mongols were called the "Golden Horde" because of their (<u>homes</u>/armor).

10. (Japanese/<u>Mongol</u>) soldiers lived in the saddle and even slept on their horses during marches.

11. (Batu Khan/<s>Tamerlane</s>) demonstrated great cruelty and built an empire that collapsed shortly after his death.

12. Chinggis Khan invaded (<u>northern</u>/southern) China.

13. (China/<s>Japan</s>) successfully repelled two Mongol invasions.

14. Cast iron was developed by the (Mongols/<u>Chinese</u>).

15. China was the first nation to use (iron/<u>paper</u>) as a form of currency.

Matching

Place the correct letter in the blank.

__B__ 16. Law code written by Chinggis Khan

__D__ 17. One of the greatest monuments of architecture in India

__C__ 18. Supposedly had power over spirits

__E__ 19. A mystical and superstitious religion

__A__ 20. Religious leader who taught a philosophy based on relationships

A. <s>Confucius</s>
B. <s>Great Yasa</s>
C. <s>shamans</s>
D. <s>Taj Mahal</s>
E. <s>Taoism</s>

Name _____

Tues. Aug 3rd

After the Fall of Rome

Who Am I?

Write the correct answer beside each statement.

Clovis 1. Became the leader of a Frankish kingdom in 481

Pepin the Short 2. Was given papal permission to have the title of king

Charlemagne 3. Was crowned Roman emperor by the pope

Charles Martel 4. Expanded Pepin II's kingdom

the pope 5. Initially known as the bishop of Rome

Pepin II 6. Mayor of the palace that conquered and united territories under Frankish rule

Carlman 7. The brother of Charlemagne

missionaries 8. Sent by the bishop of Rome to German tribes, Gaul, Spain, and Britain

What Am I?

Monasteries 9. Places where learning was preserved during feudalism

manor 10. The estate on which most people lived during the Middle Ages

Merovingian 11. The royal line started by Clovis

Carolingian 12. The royal line started by Pepin II

mayor of the palace 13. The leading palace official

feudalism 14. System where a majority of people did not own land but worked for those who did

Christianity 15. The religion propagated in Europe during the Middle Ages

Name _____

The Anglo-Saxon Chronicle

Answer the questions at the end of this enrichment activity based on the excerpts below.

The Anglo-Saxon Chronicle:

Year 1066

In this year King Harold came from York to Westminster at the Easter which was after the midwinter that the king passed away; and Easter was then on *16 April*. Then throughout all England, a sign such as men never saw before was seen in the heavens. Some men declared that it was the star *comet*, which some men call the 'haired' star; and it appeared first on the eve of the *Greater Litany*, that is on *24 April*, and shone thus all the week. And soon thereafter came Earl Tostig from beyond the sea into Wight, with as great a fleet as he could get, and there he was given both money and provisions; and then went from there, and did harm everywhere along the seacoast where he could get to, until he came to Sandwich. Then when King Harold, who was in London, was informed that his brother Tostig had come to Sandwich, he gathered a greater ship-army and also land-army than any king in the land had ever gathered before, because he was told for certain that Earl William from Normandy, relative of King Edward, wanted to come here and win this land, just as it afterwards came to pass. Then when Tostig found out that King Harold was on his way to Sandwich, he went from Sandwich, and took some of the boatmen with him, some willingly, some unwillingly; and then turned north into [the Humber], and there raided in Lindsey, and killed many good men there. Then when Earl Edwin and Earl Morcar realised that, they came there and drove him out of the land.

. . . .

Harald king of Norway and Earl Tostig went into York with as great a force as seemed to them [necessary] and they were given hostages from the town, and also help with provisions, and so went from there to ship, and spoke of complete peace provided that they would all go south with them and win this land. Then in the middle of this came Harold, king of the English, with all his army on the Sunday to Tadcaster and there marshaled his fleet; and then on Monday went right through York. And Harald, king of Norway, and Earl Tostig and their division had gone from ship beyond York to Stamford Bridge, because it had been promised them for certain that hostages would be brought to meet them there from the whole shire. Then Harold, king of the English, came upon them beyond the bridge by surprise; and there they joined battle and were fighting very hard long in the day; and there Harald, king of Norway, was killed and Earl Tostig and countless people with them, both of Northmen and of English.

. . . .

Earl William [came] up at Hastings on the Feast of St Michael and Harold . . . fought with him before all his raiding-army had come; and there [Harold] fell, and his two brothers, Gyrth and Leofwine. And William conquered this land, and came to Westminster, and Archbishop Aldred consecrated him as king. And men paid him tribute, and gave hostages, and afterwards bought their lands.

M. J. Swanton, trans. and ed. *The Anglo-Saxon Chronicle*. (New York: Routledge, 1996). 194, 196–98.

1. This chronicle mentions which English towns? (This shows that they were founded before 1066.)

   _____

2. What "sign" did the English see in the sky? How did the chronicler and the English describe it?

   _____

3. Who was the ruler of England before the Norman invasion? _____

4. Where did King Harold and his two brothers fall (in death)? _____

5. At what town was William the Conqueror crowned king? _____

6. Who consecrated William as the new king of England? _____

7. What did the English bring to William after he became their king? _____

8. What did the English buy from William after he became their king? _____

Name _____

The Canterbury Tales

Answer the questions at the end of this enrichment activity based on the following excerpts from Chaucer's works.

With him there rode a gentle pardoner*
Of Rouncival, his friend and his compeer;*
Straight from the court of Rome had journeyed he.
Loudly he sang Come hither, love, to me,
The summoner joining with a burden round;*
Was never horn of half so great a sound.
This pardoner had hair as yellow as wax,
But lank* it hung as does a strike* of flax;
In wisps hung down such locks as he'd on head,
And with them he his shoulders overspread;
But thin they dropped, and stringy, one by one.
But as to hood, for sport of it, he'd none,
Though it was packed in wallet all the while.
It seemed to him he went in latest style,
Dishevelled, save for cap, his head all bare.
As shiny eyes he had as has a hare.
He had a fine veronica* sewed to cap.
His wallet lay before him in his lap,
Stuffed full of pardons brought from Rome all hot.
A voice he had that bleated like a goat. . . . .
No beard had he, nor ever should he have,
For smooth his face as he'd just had a shave;
I think he was a gelding or a mare.
But in his craft, from Berwick unto Ware,
Was no such pardoner in any place.
For in his bag he had a pillowcase
The which, he said, was Our True Lady's veil:
He said he had a piece of the very sail
That good Saint Peter had, what time he went
Upon the sea, till Jesus changed his bent.
He had a latten* cross set full of stones,
And in a bottle had he some pig's bones.
But with these relics, when he came upon
Some simple parson, then this paragon*
In that one day more money stood to gain
Than the poor dupe* in two months could attain.
And thus, with flattery and suchlike japes,*
He made the parson and the rest his apes.*
But yet, to tell the whole truth at the last,
He was, in church, a fine ecclesiast.
Well could he read a lesson or a story,
But best of all he sang an offertory;
For well he knew that when that song was sung,
Then might he preach, and all with polished tongue.
To win some silver, as he right well could;
Therefore he sang so merrily and so loud.

pardoner: a person who sells indulgences and other items to raise money for the Roman Church
compeer: companion

burden round: strong bass voice

lank: straight, flat / *strike*: strip

veronica: According to Catholic tradition, Veronica wiped the face of Christ, and an image of His face remained on the cloth.

latten: thin, brass-like metal

this paragon: the pardoner

the . . . dupe: the parson
japes: tricks
apes: fools

www.canterburytales.org. (Excerpt from the *General Prologue*, lines 671–90 and 694–716)

1. From where did the pardoner come (or claim to have come)? _____

2. What objects does he carry in a bottle? _____

3. What other "holy relics" does he bring with him? _____
   _____

4. When he comes to a village, whom does he trick and make like fools? _____
   _____

5. According to the end of the passage, what is the pardoner's motive for preaching in a village church?
   _____

Name _____

Crossword Puzzle

Across

2. Plague in Europe spread by poor sanitation
3. Thirteenth century architecture with flying buttresses
5. Author of *Divine Comedy*
8. Large and impressive church buildings
9. Peasant girl who rallied the French in the Hundred Years' War
10. Campaigns to liberate the Holy Land
11. New centers of liberal arts learning that began in the twelfth century
13. Common spoken languages
14. Document carried on a journey and exchanged for money at a bank

Down

1. Calamity that overwhelmed Europe in 1315 and resulted from massive crop spoilage
4. Author of *The Canterbury Tales*
6. Places for exchanging or borrowing money
7. Commonly found in artwork and used to represent holiness
10. Strict code that governed a knight's behavior
12. Religious group that the Crusades targeted on the Iberian Peninsula

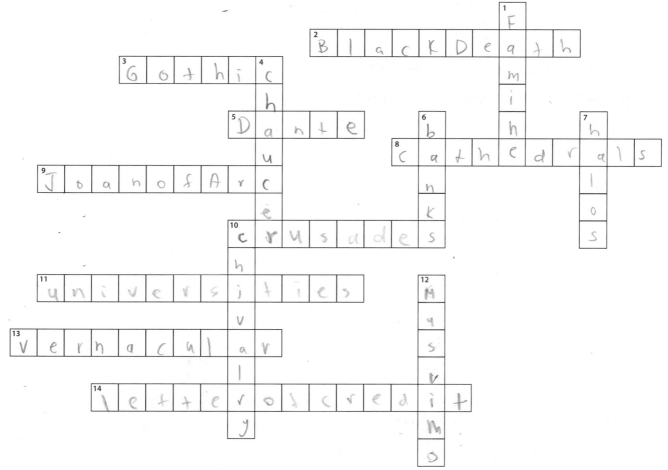

Across answers filled in: 2. Black Death; 3. Gothic; 5. Dante; 8. Cathedrals; 9. Joan of Arc; 10. Crusades; 11. Universities; 13. Vernacular; 14. Letters of credit

Down answers filled in: 1. Famine; 4. Chaucer; 6. Banks; 7. Halos; 10. Chivalry; 12. Muslims

Name _____

Chapter Review

Completion

Underline the term that accurately completes each statement.

1. (Castles/<u>Towns</u>) grew along trade routes.

2. Europe experienced a warm period that allowed farmers to grow (<u>more</u>/less) crops.

3. (<u>Venice</u>/Paris) developed a city-state with a republican form of government.

4. The Crusades (succeeded/<u>failed</u>) in freeing the Holy Land.

5. Chaucer was an (<u>English</u>/Italian) poet.

6. The English used (heavy armor/<u>longbows</u>) to defeat the French in battle.

7. (Romanesque/<u>Gothic</u>) architecture used flying buttresses and stained glass windows.

8. Bankers issued (interdicts/<u>letters of credit</u>) to traveling merchants.

9. The Roman Church lost credibility when it could not stop the (<u>Black Death</u>/Hundred Years' War).

10. The Knights Templar protected traveling (bankers/<u>pilgrims</u>).

11. (<u>William the Conqueror</u>/Hugh Capet) conquered England and established a new dynasty.

12. Henry II strengthened royal authority in (<u>England</u>/France).

13. (<u>Romanesque</u>/Gothic) architecture was described as dark and cold.

14. The Reconquista occurred in (France/<u>Spain</u>).

15. The common spoken languages of the people are known as (<u>the vernacular</u>/chivalry).

Matching

Place the correct letter in the blank.

_C_ 16. Brought the medieval papacy to its peak

_D_ 17. Signed the Magna Carta

_B_ 18. Established circuit courts

_E_ 19. Sent out royal officials called baillis

_A_ 20. English king that tried to claim the French throne

A. Edward III
B. Henry II
C. Innocent III
D. King John
E. Philip II

Name _____

Utopia

Answer the questions below based on the following excerpts from Sir Thomas More's work.

[*On proper punishment*]

I answered, "It seems to me a very unjust thing to take away a man's life for a little money, for nothing in the world can be of equal value with a man's life: and if it be said, 'that it is not for the money that one suffers, but for his breaking the law," I must say, extreme justice is an extreme injury: for we ought not to approve of those terrible laws that make the smallest offences capital, nor of that opinion of the Stoics that makes all crimes equal; as if there were no difference to be made between the killing [of] a man and the taking [of] his purse, between which, if we examine things impartially, there is no likeness nor proportion. God has commanded us not to kill, and shall we kill so easily for a little money? . . . [Since God has] taken from us the right of disposing either of our own or of other people's lives, if it is pretended that the mutual consent of men in making laws can authorise man-slaughter in cases in which God has given us no example, that it frees people from the obligation of the divine law, and so makes murder a lawful action, what is this, but to give a preference to human laws before the divine? and, if this is once admitted, by the same rule men may, in all other things, put what restrictions they please upon the laws of God."

The Utopia by Sir Thomas More. Public Domain.

1 According to More, what crime should not be punishable by death? _____

2. Why is the death penalty too harsh for this crime? _____

_____

3. Does More believe that man has the right to kill himself or anyone else? _____

[*On the limited rights of kings*]

Now what if, after all these propositions were made, I should rise up and assert that such counsels were both unbecoming a king and [harmful] to him; and that not only his honour, but his safety, consisted more in his people's wealth than in his own; if I should show that they choose a king for their own sake, and not for his; that, by his care and endeavours, they may be both easy and safe; and that, therefore, a prince ought to take more care of his people's happiness than of his own, as a shepherd is to take more care of his flock than of himself? It is also certain that they are much mistaken that think the poverty of a nation is a mean[s] of the public safety. Who quarrel more than beggars? who does more earnestly long for a change than he that is uneasy in his present circumstances? and who run to create confusions with so desperate a boldness as those who, having nothing to lose, hope to gain by them? If a king should fall under such contempt or envy that he could not keep his subjects in their duty but by oppression and ill usage, and by rendering them poor and miserable, it were certainly better for him to quit his kingdom than to retain it by such methods as make him, while he keeps the name of authority, lose the majesty due to it. Nor is it so becoming the dignity of a king to reign over beggars as over rich and happy subjects. And therefore Fabricius, a man of a noble and exalted temper, said "he would rather govern rich men than be rich himself; since for one man to abound in wealth and pleasure when all about him are mourning and groaning, is to be a [jailer] and not a king." He is an unskilful physician that cannot cure one disease without casting his patient into another. So he that can find no other way for correcting the errors of his people but by taking from them the conveniences of life, shows that he knows not what it is to govern a free nation. He himself ought rather to shake off his sloth, or to lay down his pride, for the contempt or hatred that his people have for him takes its rise from the vices in himself. Let him live upon what belongs to him without wronging others, and accommodate his expense to his revenue. Let him punish crimes, and, by his wise conduct, let him endeavour to prevent them, rather than be severe when he has suffered them to be too common.

The Utopia by Sir Thomas More. Public Domain.

4. More compares the job of a king to what three other jobs? _____

5. What does More say is the danger of having poor subjects? _____

_____

6. Does More think that it is dangerous for a king to have rich subjects? _____

Name _____

Erasmus and Access to Scripture

Answer the questions below based on the following excerpt from the introduction of Erasmus's Greek New Testament.

I strongly dissent from those who are unwilling to have the Scriptures translated into the vernacular and read by the ignorant, as if Christ taught so complicated a doctrine that it can hardly be understood even by a handful of theologians or as if the [deep secret or mystery] of the Christian religion consisted in its not being known. It is perhaps reasonable to conceal the mysteries of kings, but Christ seeks to divulge his mysteries as much as possible. I should like to have even the most humble women read [the four Gospels] and the Epistles of St. Paul. . . . Would that the plowboy recited something from them at his plowshare, that the weaver sang from them at his shuttle and that the traveler whiled away the tedium of his journey with their tales. . . .

To me he is truly a theologian who teaches not with [logic] and [twisted] arguments but . . . who teaches indeed by the example of his own life that riches are to be despised, that the Christian man must not put his faith in the defenses of this world but depend entirely on Heaven . . . [and] that all good men ought to love and cherish each other. . . . If anyone inspired by the spirit of Christ preaches things of this kind . . . then he is a true theologian even if he should be a ditch digger.

Desiderius Erasmus, "The Philosophy of Christ." *The Renaissance: Maker of Modern Man.* Ed. Kenneth M. Setton. (Washington: National Geographic Society, 1970). 300–301.

1. How does Erasmus respond to those who would restrict access to the Scripture in native languages?

   _____

2. What does Erasmus imply that the Roman Church teaches about Scripture? _____

   _____

3. According to Erasmus, who should be allowed to read the Scriptures? _____

   _____

4. Whom does Erasmus identify as a true theologian? _____

   _____

   _____

5. According to Erasmus, does one have to be extremely educated to be a theologian? Why or why not?

   _____

   _____

Name _____

"Why Monks Are Shunned"

Answer the questions below based on the following excerpts from François Rabelais's work.

"There is nothing truer than that the robe and cowl [clothing worn by monks] draw down upon themselves all sorts of hard feelings, insults, and curses on the part of everybody. . . . The chief reason is that monks feed on . . . human sins, and . . . they are always being driven back . . . to their convents and abbeys, which are isolated from polite intercourse as are the privies of a house. But if you can understand why it is that a pet monkey in a household is always teased and tormented, then you ought to be able to understand why it is that monks are shunned. . . . The monkey does not watch the house, like a dog; he does not haul a cart like the ox; he produces neither milk like the cow nor wool like the sheep; he does not carry burdens like the horse. . . .

"Similarly, a monk—I mean the lazy ones—does not labor, like the peasant; he does not guard the country like the soldier; he does not cure the sick like the doctor; he does not preach to nor teach the world like a good evangelic doctor and pedagogue [schoolmaster]; he does not bring in commodities and public necessities like the merchant. And that is the reason why they are all jeered at and [hated]."

"But . . . don't they pray [to] God for us?"

"They do nothing of the kind," said Gargantua.

"All they do is keep the whole neighborhood awake by jangling their bells."

François Rabelais. "Why Monks Are Shunned." *The Renaissance: Maker of Modern Man*. Ed. Kenneth M. Setton. (Washington: National Geographic Society, 1970). 302.

1. What two articles of clothing worn by monks attracted "hard feelings [and] insults"? _____

2. According to Rabelais, on what do the monks feed? _____

3. To what animal does Rabelais compare late medieval monks? _____

4. What kinds of workers does Rabelais describe as contributors to society? _____

   _____

5. Because the monks did not contribute to society, how did the European common people respond to them?

   _____

6. How did the monks keep neighborhoods awake at night? _____

Name _____

Luther's Ninety-Five Theses

Answer the questions below based on the following excerpts of Luther's writings.

21. Those preachers of indulgences are in error, who say that by the pope's indulgences a man is freed from every penalty and is saved. . . .

27. They preach man-made doctrines who say that so soon as the coin jingles into the money-box, the soul flies out of purgatory.

28. It is certain that when the coin jingles into the money-box, greed and avarice can be increased, but the result of the intercession of the church is in the power of God alone. . . .

32. They will be condemned eternally, together with their teachers, who believe themselves sure of their salvation because they have letters of pardon. . . .

35. They preach no Christian doctrine who teach that contrition [sorrow over sin] is not necessary in those who intend to buy souls out of purgatory or to buy confessional privileges.

36. Every truly repentant Christian has a right to full remission of penalty and guilt, even without letters of pardon.

37. Every true Christian, whether living or dead, has part in all the benefits of Christ and the church; and this is granted to him by God, even without letters of pardon. . . .

43. Christians are to be taught that he who gives to the poor or lends to the needy does a better work than buying pardons. . . .

45. Christians are to be taught that he who sees a man in need and passes him by and gives his money for pardons instead, purchases not the indulgences of the pope, but the indignation [anger] of God. . . .

50. Christians are to be taught that if the pope knew the exactions [excessive demands] of the indulgence preachers, he would rather that St. Peter's church should go to ashes than that it should be built up with the skin, flesh, and bones of his sheep.

51. Christians are to be taught that it would be the pope's wish, as it is his duty, to give of his own money to many of those from whom certain hawkers of pardons cajole money, even though the church of St. Peter might have to be sold. . . .

54. Injury is done to the Word of God when, in the same sermon, an equal or a longer time is spent on pardons than on the Word.

55. It must be the pope's intention that if pardons, which are a very small thing, are celebrated with one bell, single processions, and ceremonies, then the gospel, which is the very greatest thing, should be preached with a hundred bells, a hundred processions, and a hundred ceremonies.

Reprinted from *Martin Luther's Ninety-Five Theses* by Stephen J. Nichols, copyright 2002, P&R Publishing, Phillipsburg, NJ. Used with permission from P&R Publishing Co. PO Box 817, Phillipsburg, N.J. 08865. www.prpbooks.com.

1. According to indulgence-sellers, what happened when money fell into the money collection box?
   The soul flies out of purgatory

2. What does Luther say will happen to those who think they are saved because they have "letters of pardon" (indulgences)? They will be condemned eternally.

3. What is a necessary attitude for those who buy indulgences or confessional privileges? Sorrow over sin

4. What good work is better than buying pardons for sin? _giving the money to the poor._

5. What does Luther think the pope would do if he knew how indulgences were being abused? _he would rather St Peters be burned._

6. What two spiritual things are more important and deserve more attention than proclaiming and selling indulgences? _The Word of God and the gospel._

Name _____

Chapter Review

Underline the word or phrase that makes the statement correct.

1. The Renaissance started in (Spain/Italy).

2. The fall of (Venice/Constantinople) contributed to a revival of learning in Europe.

3. The Bible was first translated into English by (Wycliffe/Luther).

4. The Reformation began in (Germany/Italy).

5. Church courts which sought to find and punish heresy were held during (transubstantiation/the Inquisition).

6. The Roman Church burned (Wycliffe/Huss) at the stake.

7. Castiglione wrote a book about Renaissance (warfare/manners).

8. Erasmus published a (Greek/German) New Testament.

9. Lorenzo de Medici generously supported the (Renaissance/Reformation).

10. (Machiavelli/Erasmus) exposed corruption in the Roman Church with his work *In Praise of Folly*.

11. Zwingli was a reformer in (Germany/Switzerland).

12. (Zwingli/Luther) was the author of the Ninety-five Theses.

13. (Transubstantiation/Excommunication) is the teaching that the bread and wine in the Lord's Supper change into the body and blood of Christ.

14. (Inquisitions/Indulgences) were papers that granted pardon from the punishment of sin.

15. Pope (Leo X/Martin V) authorized the issuing of indulgences to pay for the completion of St. Peter's Basilica.

16. Pope (Gregory VII/Boniface VIII) demanded submission to the pope as a requirement for salvation.

17. (Michelangelo/Leonardo da Vinci) painted *The Last Supper*.

18. (Michelangelo/Gutenberg) painted the ceiling of Rome's Sistine Chapel.

19. (Brunelleschi/Ghiberti) designed the dome of the Cathedral of Florence.

20. (Gutenberg/Erasmus) invented the movable-type printing press.

Name _____

Christopher Columbus

Answer the questions at the end based on the following excerpts from Columbus's journal.

Friday, 3rd of August

We departed on Friday, the 3rd of August, in the year 1492, from the bar of Saltes, at 8 o'clock, and proceeded with a strong sea breeze until sunset, towards the south, for 60 miles, equal to 15 leagues; afterwards S.W. and W.S.W., which was the course for the Canaries.

Sunday, 9th of September

This day the Admiral [traveled] 19 leagues, and he arranged to [record] less . . . because if the voyage was of long duration, the people would not be so terrified and disheartened. . . .

Monday, 17th of September

. . . They saw much very fine grass and herbs from rocks, which came from the west. They, therefore, considered that they were near land. The pilots observed the north point, and found that the needles turned a full point to the west of north. So the mariners were alarmed and dejected, and did not give their reason. But the Admiral knew, and ordered that the north should be observed at dawn. They then found that the needles were true. The cause was that the star makes the movement, and not the needles. . . .

Wednesday, 26th of September

The Admiral continued on the west course until after noon. Then he altered course to S.W., until he made out that what had been said to be land was only clouds. Day and night they made 31 leagues, counting 24 for the people. The sea was like a river, the air pleasant and very mild.

Saturday, 6th of October

The Admiral continued his west course, and during day and night they [traveled] 40 leagues, 33 being counted. This night Martin Alonso said that it would be well to steer south of west, and it appeared to the Admiral that Martin Alonso did not say this with respect to the island of Cipango. He saw that if an error was made the land would not be reached so quickly, and that consequently it would be better to go at once to the continent and afterwards to the islands.

Thursday, 11th of October

The course was W.S.W., and there was [rougher] sea than there had been during the whole of the voyage. They saw sandpipers, and a green reed near the ship. Those of the caravel *Pinta* saw a cane and a pole, and they took up another small pole which appeared to have been worked with iron; also another bit of cane, a land-plant, and a small board. The crew of the caravel *Niña* also saw signs of land, and a small branch covered with berries. Everyone breathed afresh and rejoiced at these signs. The run until sunset was 26 leagues.

After sunset the Admiral returned to his original west course, and they went along at the rate of 12 miles an hour. Up to two hours after midnight they had gone 90 miles, equal to 22½ leagues. As the caravel *Pinta* was a better sailer, and went ahead of the Admiral, she found the land, and made the signals ordered by the Admiral. The land was first seen by a sailor named Rodrigo de Triana. But the Admiral, at ten in the previous night, being on the castle of the poop, saw a light, though it was so uncertain that he could not affirm it was land. He called Pero Gutierrez, a gentleman of the King's bedchamber, and said that there seemed to be a light, and that he should look at it. He did so, and saw it. The Admiral said the same to Rodrigo Sanchez of Segovia, whom the King and Queen had sent with the fleet as inspector, but he could see nothing, because he was not in a place whence anything could be seen. After the Admiral had spoken he saw a light once or twice, and it was like a wax candle rising and falling. It seemed to few to be an indication of land; but the Admiral made certain that land was close. . . .

Having landed, they saw trees very green, and much water, and fruits of diverse kinds. The Admiral called to the two captains, and to the others who leaped on shore, and to Rodrigo Escovedo, secretary of the whole fleet, and to Rodrigo Sanchez of Segovia, and said that they should bear faithful testimony that he, in presence of all, had taken, as he now took, possession of the said island for the King and for the Queen, his Lords making the declarations that are required, as is more largely set forth in the testimonies which were then made in writing.

Presently many inhabitants of the island assembled. What follows is in the actual words of the Admiral in his book of the first navigation and discovery of the Indies. "I," he says, "that we might form great friendship, for I knew that they were a people who could be more easily freed and converted to our holy faith by love than by force, gave to some of them red caps, and glass beads to put round their necks, and many other things of little value, which gave them great pleasure, and made them so much our friends that it was a marvel to see. They afterwards came to the ship's boats where we were, swimming and bringing us parrots, cotton threads in skeins, darts, and many other things; and we exchanged them for other things that we gave them, such as glass beads and small bells. In fine, they took all, and gave what they had with good will. . . ."

Clements R. Markham, trans. *The Journal of Christopher Columbus: During His First Voyage 1492–1493* (London: Hakluyt Society, 1893), pp. 18, 22, 24, 30, 33, 35–37. Available at Google Books: http://books.google.com/books?id=2mvK60VAdCcC&printsec=frontcover - v=onepage&q&f=false

1. What did Columbus do to keep his men from realizing how far they were traveling? *Columbus logged less distance than they actualy travelled.*

2. Why were the men alarmed on September 17th? _____

_____

3. What signs showed Columbus and his men that they were close to land? _____

_____

_____

4. On what day did Columbus and his men experience the roughest weather of the voyage? _____

_____

5. Why did Columbus give the islanders gifts? _____

_____

Name _____

Bartolomé de Las Casas

Answer the questions at the end based on the following excerpts from Las Casas's writings.

The Lucayan Islands on the North Side, adjacent to Hispaniola [Dominican Republic and Haiti] and Cuba, which are Sixty in number, or thereabout, together with . . . those, [commonly] known by the name of the Gigantic Isles, and others, the most infertile whereof, exceeds the Royal Garden of Sevil in fruitfulness, a most Healthful and pleasant Climat[e], is now laid waste and uninhabited; and whereas, when the Spaniards first arriv'd here, about Five Hundred Thousand Men dwelt in it, they are now cut off, some by slaughter, and others ravished away by Force and Violence, to work in the Mines of Hispanioloa, which was destitute of Native Inhabitants: For a certain Vessel, sailing to this Isle, to the end, that the Harvest being over (some good Christian, moved with Piety and Pity, undertook this dangerous Voyage, to convert Souls to Christianity) the remaining gleanings might be gathered up, there were only found Eleven Persons, which I saw with my own Eyes. There are other Islands Thirty in number, and upward bordering upon the Isle of St. John [San Juan, today Puerto Rico], totally unpeopled; all which are above Two Thousand miles in [length], and yet remain without Inhabitants, Native, or People.

As to the firm land, we are certainly satisfied, and assur'd, that the Spaniards by their barbarous and [horrible] Actions have absolutely depopulated Ten Kingdoms, of greater extent than all Spain, together with the Kingdoms of Arragon and Portugal, that is to say, above One Thousand Miles, which now [lie] wast[e] and desolate, and are absolutely ruined, when as formerly no other Country whatsoever was more populous. Nay we dare boldly affirm, that during the Forty Years space, wherein [the Spaniards] exercised their [bloody] and detestable Tyranny in these Regions, above Twelve Millions ([of] Men, Women, and Children) have undeservedly perished; nor do I conceive that I should deviate from the Truth by saying that above Fifty Millions in all paid their last Debt to Nature.

Those that arriv'd at these Islands from the remotest parts of Spain, and who pride themselves in the Name of Christians, steer'd Two courses principally, in order to the [murder], and Exterminating of this People from the face of the Earth. The first whereof was raising an unjust, [bloody], cruel War. The other, by putting them to death, who . . . thirsted after their Liberty, or design'd to recover their [pristine] Freedom, and shake off the Shackles of so injurious a Captivity: For they being taken off in War, none but Women and Children were permitted to enjoy the benefit of that Country-Air, [on] whom they did in succeeding times lay such a heavy [yoke], that the very Brutes [animals] were more happy than they. . . .

Now the ultimate end and scope that incited the Spaniards to endeavor the [killing] and Desolation of this People, was Gold only; that thereby growing [wealthy] in a short time, they might arrive at once at such Degrees and Dignities, [that were not] consistent with their Persons.

Finally, in one word, their Ambition and [covetousness] . . . and the vast Wealth of those Regions; the Humility and Patience of the Inhabitants (which made their approach to these Lands more [effortless] and [easy]) did much promote the business: Whom they so despicably [hated], that they treated them (I speak of things which I was an Eye Witness of, without the least fallacy) not as Beasts, which I cordially wished they would, but as the most abject dung and filth of the Earth; and so [demanding] they were of their Life and Soul, that the above-mentioned number of People died without understanding the true Faith or Sacraments. And this also is as really true as the [preceding] Narration (which the very Tyrants and cruel Murderers cannot deny without the stigma of a [lie]) that the Spaniards never received any injury from the Indians, but that [the Indians] rather reverenced them as Persons descended from Heaven, until [the Indians] were compelled to take up Arms, provoked thereunto by repeated Injuries, violent Torments, and [unjust] Butcheries.

A Brief Account of the Destruction of the Indies by Bartolomé de Las Casas. Public Domain.

1. Which islands are mentioned in this passage? What are the current names of some of these islands?

   _____

2. According to Las Casas, how many Indians were killed by the Spanish and made to pay "their last Debt to Nature"? _____

3. Why did the Spanish conquistadors abuse the Indians? How does this illustrate 1 Timothy 6:10?

   _____

   _____

4. According to the end of this excerpt, what did the Indians first think of the Spanish? _____

   _____

Name _____

Chapter Review

Completion

Underline the word or phrase that accurately completes the statement.

1. (Siam/Dai Viet) is the ancient name for Thailand.

2. The (Aztecs/Mayas) stoned adulterers and placed great importance on the family.

3. (Dias/Columbus) was the first explorer to find a way around the tip of Africa.

4. Atahualpa was the last (Mayan/Incan) ruler before the Spanish arrived.

5. (Tenochtitlán/Cuzco) was the capital city of the Aztec Empire.

6. (Cortés/Pizarro) conquered the Incan Empire.

7. Queen (Isabella/Elizabeth) financed Sir Francis Drake's expeditions.

8. The (Spanish/Portuguese) developed a thriving trade with India.

9. The Aztecs expected the return of the god (Cuzco/Quetzalcoatl).

10. Indians in Southwest North America lived in villages called (pueblos/effigy mounds).

11. The Iroquois Confederacy was located in the modern state of (Georgia/New York).

12. The American Indians who migrated with the herds and did not build permanent settlements lived on the (East Coast/Great Plains).

13. (Magellan/Dias) gave the Pacific Ocean its name.

14. Sailors used the (astrolabe/compass) to determine direction when plotting a course.

15. Spain and Portugal are located by the (Pacific/Atlantic) Ocean.

Matching

Place the correct letter in each blank.

___A___ 16. New type of ship with triangular sails

___E___ 17. Jesuit missionary to Japan

___B___ 18. Capital of the Incan empire

___C___ 19. Mythical Christian king that explorers sought in Africa

___D___ 20. Catholic missionary to the Americas that was an advocate for the Indians.

A. caravel
B. Cuzco
C. Prester John
D. Bartolomé de Las Casas
E. Francis Xavier

Name _____   65

Why the Pilgrims Left the Netherlands

Answer the questions below based on the following excerpt from Bradford's writings.

After [the Pilgrims] had lived in [Leiden] about some 11 or 12 years, . . . and [some] of them were taken away by death; and many others begane to be well striken in years, . . . those prudent governours with [various] of [the oldest] members begane both deeply to apprehend their present dangers, and wisely to foresee the future, and thinke of [a timely] remedy. In the agitation of their thoughts, and much discours[e] of things hear aboute, at length they began to incline to this conclusion, of remooval to some other place. Not out of any newfanglednes, or other [such] like giddie humor, by which men are oftentimes transported to their great hurt, and danger. But for [various] weightie and solid reasons; some of the cheefe of which I will hear breefly touch. [First], they saw and found by experience the hardnes[s] of the place and countrie to be [such], as few in comparison would come to them; and fewer that would bide it out, and continew with them. For many that came to them, and many more that desired to be with them; could not endure that great labor and hard fare, with other inconveniences which they underwent and were contented with. . . . For many, though they desired to [enjoy] the ordinances of God in their puritie, and the libertie of the gospell with them, yet (alas) they . . . preferred, and chose the prisons in England, rather [than] this libertie in Holland, with these afflictions. . . .

[Secondly]. They saw, that though the people generally, bore all these difficulties very cherfully, and with a resolute courage, being in the best, and strength of their years, yet old age began to steale on many of them, (and their great and continuall labours, with other crosses and sorrows, hastened it before the time) so as it was not only probably thought, but apparently seen, that within a few years more, they would be in danger to scatter (by necessities pressing them) or sinke under their burdens, or both. . . .

Thirdly; As necessitie was a taskmaster over them, so they were forced to be [such], not only to their servants (but in a sorte) to their dearest chilldren; the which as it did . . . wound the tender [hearts] of many a loving father, and mother, so it produced likwise [various] sad and sorowfull effects. For many of their children, that were of best dispositions, and gracious Inclination; (haveing lernde to bear the yoake in their youth) and willing to bear parte of their parents burden, were (often times) so oppressed with their hevie labours, that though their minds were free and willing, yet their bodies bowed under the weight of the same, and became [decrepit] in their early youth; the vigor of nature being consumed in the very budd as it were. But that which was more lamentable, and of all sorowes most heavie to be borne, was that many of their children, by these occasions, and the great [immorality] of youth in [the Netherlands], and the manifold temptations of the place, were drawne away by evill examples into extravagante and dangerous courses, getting the [reins] off their [necks], and departing from their parents. Some became souldiers, others tooke . . . by sea, and other some worse courses, tending to [sinful living] and the danger of their soules, to the great greefe of their parents and dishonour of God. So that they saw their posteritie would be in danger to degenerate and be corrupted.

Lastly, (and which was not least,) a great hope, and inward zeall they had of laying some good foundation, (or at least to make some way thereunto) for the propagating, and advancing the gospel of the kingdom of Christ in those remote parts of the world; yea, though they should be but even as stepping-stones, unto others for the performing of so great a work.

These, and some other like reasons, moved them to undertake this resolution of their removall; the which they afterward [accomplished] with so great difficulties, as by the sequell will appeare.

The place they had thoughts on, was some of those vast, and unpeopled countries of America, which are frutfull, and fitt for habitation; being devoyd of all civill inhabitants; [where there] are only [savage], and brutish men, which range up and downe, [like] the wild beasts of the same.

William Bradford. *History of Plymouth Plantation 1620-1647*. Vol 1 (of 2). Ed. Worthington C. Ford, et al. (Boston: Houghton Mifflin Company, 1912). pp. 52–56. (https://archive.org/details/historyplymouth01socigoog)

1. How long did the Pilgrims live in Leiden before they decided to look for a new place to live? _____
   11-12 years

2. What condition did some Pilgrims prefer over liberty with hardship in Holland? _____
   the prisons in England

3. What happened to some of the Pilgrims' children? they wore themselves
   out in helping and left their parents.

4. What kind of spiritual influence did the Dutch have on these children? they had
   an evil influence

5. What evangelistic motives led the Pilgrims to move to America? they wanted to
   do mission work.

6. How does Bradford describe America? vast and unpeopled
   _____

7. How does Bradford describe the Indian civilizations? Evaluate this description based on what you have
   read about Indians in the Americas. _____
   _____
   _____

Name _____

Simón Bolívar

Answer the questions below based on the following excerpts from Bolívar's writings about South America.

The battle of Leipzig has at last produced the decision of a long-drawn contest in which the larger interests of the continent of Europe and the cause of the Independence of Nations have triumphed over the ambition of Bonaparte, overturning that immense colossus of French power. Of the half million Frenchmen who set out to demolish the coalition of the powers, only fifty thousand have managed to survive. The great army, the invincible eagles, the great marshals have virtually disappeared. The days of October 17, 18, 19, and 20, of the year 1813, will remain the most memorable in all the history of Europe, for during those days was won the liberty of the world, which had been threatened with invasion by the common oppressor [Napoleon].

Let America rejoice in the triumph of the allied armies, which have so gloriously defended the cause of independence. Let her cease to fear plans which Spain is in no position to carry out. The war has exhausted Spain's treasury; and the gains won from the French, while they may increase her territorial possessions, cannot give [Spain] the navy which she lacks and without which her threats against us need not be taken seriously. On the other hand, the [dominance] that the great successes of the Duke of Wellington and of the allies give Great Britain over the affairs of Spain will eventually destroy the latter's schemes against the independence of the New World. Let none fear lest that powerful nation which, even in adversity, has persistently defended the independence of Europe, should fail to defend that of America, if attacked. Let us, on the contrary, rejoice in the irresistible ascendancy that England is about to assume over both hemispheres in guarantee of universal freedom.

Our industry, hitherto of no value, and our lagging agriculture will shake off their apathy in response to the rewards afforded the farmer by the rise in the prices of the products he cultivates. Once the ports of continental Europe are thrown open to British vessels, our farmers will export our coffee, cacao, indigo, cotton, and the like, which are in great demand. Maritime commerce having been so long suppressed wherever the Napoleonic influence has extended, Europe has suffered the want [lack] of products which have become as primary a necessity for them as their exports are for us. This trade is the foundation for the prosperity of our commerce and agriculture.

The policies and the mercantile interests of England and Spain are . . . opposed with respect to America. Spain, unable to keep us tranquilly enslaved, is now bent upon our destruction; England, favoring our independence, is interested in our prosperity. The northern and southern regions of the New World are determined to maintain their freedom at all costs. Even if Spain were to dispatch the most powerful of armies, only mutual destruction could possibly result, for they could never conquer us. England would not tolerate an odious [unwanted] and, at best, futile war which, offering no hopes for Spain, could only devastate this fair half of the earth.

Yet, where are those armies? Is Spain perchance anything more than a phantom nation? With what resources can she raise these armies and transport them a distance of two thousand leagues, in order to wage a war as long as it would be hopeless? Spain is even less powerful since she repelled the French. Her efforts were those of a dying man, who, having made them, relapses into greater weakness.

England, appropriately, is today supporting Spain. In England's shadow, America can assert her freedom. England, by her influence over [Spain], ends the plans of vengeance and extermination that inspire it; and, at the same time, by her victories over thwarted France, she eliminates the last of Napoleon's designs against us. With Spain a vassal state, the Emperor of the French would not have renounced the rights that he had claimed over America, a dependency of Spain. On the contrary, his unbounded ambition would have sought . . . dominion over both Spain and America.

Simón Bolívar. *Selected Writings of Bolívar.* Vol. 1. Comp. Vicente Lecuna. Trans. Lewis Bertrand. Ed. Harold A. Bierck, Jr. (New York: The Colonial Press, Inc., 1951). 69–71.

1. In what battle did Europe defeat Napoleon's forces? _____

2. How does Bolívar describe Napoleon throughout this letter? _____

   _____

3. On what memorable days was the "liberty of the world" won? _____

4. Which nation, because it lacked both a large navy and a rich treasury, could not attack South America?

   _____

5. Which nation promised "universal freedom" and, as Bolívar expected, would protect liberty in South

   America? _____

6. How did the end of Napoleon's power in Europe help commerce and agriculture in South America?

   _____

7. What products from South America were popular and needed in Europe? _____

   _____

Name _____

European Exploration of the Americas

Write the correct letter in the blank.

A. cash crops	E. haciendas	I. Treaty of Tordesillas
B. Constitution	F. Latin America	J. War for Independence
C. donatarios	G. Line of Demarcation	
D. established church	H. *peninsulares*	

_I_ 1. Agreement between Spain and Portugal about areas for exploration

_C_ 2. Nobles that ruled Portuguese colonies

_A_ 3. Sold for cash or supplies

_F_ 4. Dominated by Spanish and Portuguese exploration

_G_ 5. Drawn by the pope to divide areas for Portuguese and Spanish exploration

_B_ 6. Document explaining the U.S. system of government

_H_ 7. Spaniards born in Spain

_E_ 8. Large country estates owned by the wealthy

_J_ 9. Delivered the thirteen colonies from English rule

_D_ 10. Recognized and supported by a colony's government

Name _____

Chapter Review

Completion

Underline the word or phrase that correctly completes the statement.

1. The Pilgrims founded the (Massachusetts Bay/<u>Plymouth</u>) Colony.

2. Brazil was colonized by the (<u>Portuguese</u>/Spanish).

3. (<u>Sugar</u>/Tobacco) was an important export of colonial Latin America.

4. (Spain/<u>Portugal</u>) ruled a colony in South America that was eighty times its size.

5. (Thousands/<u>Millions</u>) of Africans were enslaved and taken to South America.

6. (<u>France</u>/England) was the first European country to colonize modern Canada.

7. (Portugal/<u>Spain</u>) colonized the western regions of South America.

8. (<u>Antonio José de Sucre</u>/Pedro I) liberated Ecuador.

9. Ecuador was part of the (<u>New</u>/Old) World.

10. Massachusetts Bay Colony was founded by the (Pilgrims/<u>Puritans</u>).

11. The (<u>viceroy</u>/caudillo) was the colonial ruler who represented the king of Spain.

12. (<u>Mestizos</u>/Creoles) were children of Indian and Spanish parents.

13. (<u>Gauchos</u>/Barrios) were Argentinean cowboys.

14. The (Dominican/<u>Jesuit</u>) Catholic order became rich and established monopolies in South America.

15. (<u>Portugal</u>/Spain) bought slaves in Africa and took them to Europe and the New World.

Matching

Write the correct leter in the blank.

_D_ 16. Former member of the Spanish army who fought with a troop of gauchos

_E_ 17. Established Rhode Island

_A_ 18. Ambassador to England and Latin American revolutionary

_B_ 19. Known as the Father of New France

_C_ 20. A strong leader in the Jamestown colony

A. Simón Bolívar
B. Samuel de Champlain
C. Sir Thomas Dale
D. José de San Martín
E. Roger Williams

Name _____

The English Bill of Rights

Answer the questions below based on the following excerpts from the English Bill of Rights.

Declarations of the Rights of English Subjects:

That the pretended power of suspending the laws or the execution of laws by regal authority without consent of Parliament is illegal;

That the pretended power of dispensing with laws or the execution of laws by regal authority, as it hath been assumed and exercised of late, is illegal;

That the commission for erecting the late Court of Commissioners for Ecclesiastical Causes, and all other commissions and courts of like nature, are illegal and pernicious [harmful];

That levying money for or to the use of the Crown by pretence of prerogative, without grant of Parliament, for longer time, or in other manner than the same is or shall be granted, is illegal;

That it is the right of the subjects to petition the king, and all commitments [imprisonments] and prosecutions for such petitioning are illegal;

That the raising or keeping [of] a standing army within the kingdom in time of peace, unless it be with consent of Parliament, is against [the] law;

That the subjects which are Protestants may have arms for their defence suitable to their conditions and as allowed by law;

That election of members of Parliament ought to be free;

That the freedom of speech and debates or proceedings in Parliament ought not to be impeached or questioned in any court or place out of Parliament;

That excessive bail ought not to be required, nor excessive fines imposed, nor cruel and unusual punishments inflicted;

That jurors ought to be duly impanelled [selected from a list of eligible citizens] and returned, and jurors which pass upon men in trials for high treason ought to be freeholders;

That all grants and promises [payments] of fines and forfeitures of particular persons before conviction are illegal and void;

And that for redress of all grievances, and for the amending, strengthening and preserving of the laws, Parliaments ought to be held frequently.

http://avalon.law.yale.edu/17th_century/england.asp

1. What did the English oppose the king's "raising or keeping . . . in time of peace"? _Standing army_

2. What were Protestant English citizens allowed to possess in order to defend themselves? _weapons_

3. According to this document, what should not be "impeached or questioned" in any court outside of Parliament? _freedom of speech, debates, and proceedings in Parliament_

4. Based on this document, could English subjects safely ask the king for help without threat of punishment? Why or why not? _Yes_

5. What limits did the English set on bail, fines, and punishment? _punishment should not be cruel._

6. According to this document, should anyone be forced to pay a fine or forfeit his goods before being convicted? _no_

7. Why should Parliaments be held frequently? _____

_____

Name _____

Ruling Powers in Europe

If the statement is true, write the word *true* in the blank. If it is false, change the bold word(s)
to make the statement true.

Russia 1. Catherine the Great was the monarch of **Austria**.

true 2. The **Dutch** and the English did not have centralized monarchy.

Louis XIV 3. **Louis XV** was one of the most successful absolute monarchs.

high 4. The social and financial cost of absolute monarchies was **low**.

true 5. **Oliver Cromwell** led an army during the English Civil War.

after 6. The Glorious Revolution occurred **before** the English Civil War.

William & Mary 7. **James II** signed the English Bill of Rights.

true 8. Charles II came to the **English** throne after Cromwell's death.

true 9. Maria Theresa increased governmental control and improved **peasant conditions**.

Charles's 10. The Scots defeated **James's** forces when the English invaded Scotland.

Name _____

Galileo's Observations

Answer the questions below based on the following excerpts from the writings of Galileo.

The Starry Messenger

About ten months ago a report reached my ears that a certain Fleming* had constructed a spyglass by means of which visible objects, though very distant from the eye of the observer, were distinctly seen as if nearby. Of this truly remarkable effect several experiences were related, to which some persons gave credence while others denied them. A few days later the report was confirmed to me in a letter from a noble Frenchman at Paris, Jacques Badovere, which caused me to apply myself wholeheartedly to inquire into the means by which I might arrive at the invention of a similar instrument. This I did shortly afterwards, my basis being the theory of refraction. First I prepared a tube of lead, at the ends of which I fitted two glass lenses, both plane on one side while on the other side one was spherically convex and the other concave. Then placing my eye near the concave lens I perceived objects satisfactorily large and near, for they appeared three times closer and nine times larger than when seen with the naked eye alone. Next I constructed another one, more accurate, which represented objects as enlarged more than sixty times. Finally, sparing neither labor nor expense, I succeeded in constructing for myself so excellent an instrument that objects seen by means of it appeared nearly one thousand times larger and over thirty times closer than when regarded with our natural vision.

*Fleming: a native of Flanders, the Flemish-speaking portion of Belgium

It would be [unnecessary] to enumerate the number and importance of the advantages of such an instrument at sea as well as on land. But forsaking terrestrial [earthly] observations, I turned to celestial [heavenly] ones, and first I saw the moon from as near at hand as if it were scarcely two terrestrial radii away. After that I observed often with wondering delight both the planets and the fixed stars, and since I saw these latter to be very crowded, I began to seek (and eventually found) a method by which I might measure their distances apart. . . .

Now let us review the observations made during the past two months, once more inviting the attention of all who are eager for true philosophy to the first steps of such important contemplations. Let us speak first of that surface of the moon which faces us. For greater clarity I distinguish two parts of this surface, a lighter and a darker; the lighter part seems to surround and to pervade the whole hemisphere, while the darker part discolors the moon's surface like a kind of cloud, and makes it appear covered with spots. Now those spots which are fairly dark and rather large are plain to everyone and have been seen throughout the ages; these I shall call the "large" or "ancient" spots, distinguishing them from others that are smaller in size but so numerous as to occur all over the lunar surface, and especially the lighter part. The latter spots had never been seen by anyone before me. From observations of these spots repeated many times I have been led to the opinion and conviction that the surface of the moon is not smooth, uniform, and precisely spherical as a great number of philosophers believe it (and the other heavenly bodies) to be, but is uneven, rough, and full of cavities and prominences, being not unlike the face of the earth, [containing] chains of mountains and deep valleys. . . .

On the seventh day of January in this present year 1610, at the first hour of night, when I was viewing the heavenly bodies with a telescope, Jupiter presented itself to me; and because I had prepared a very excellent instrument for myself, I perceived (as I had not before, on account of the weakness of my previous instrument) that beside the planet there were three starlets, small indeed, but very bright. Though I believed them to be among the host of fixed stars, they aroused my curiosity somewhat by appearing to lie in an exact straight line parallel to the ecliptic, and by their being more splendid than others of their size. . . . The most easterly star and the western one appeared larger than the other. I paid no attention to the distances between them and Jupiter, for at the outset I thought them to be fixed stars, as I have said. But returning to the same investigation on January eighth—led by what, I do not know—I found a very different arrangement. The three starlets were now all to the west of Jupiter, closer together, and at equal intervals from one another. . . .

I had now decided beyond all question that there existed in the heavens three stars wandering about Jupiter as do Venus and Mercury about the sun, and this became plainer than daylight from observations on similar occasions which followed. Nor were there just three such stars; four wanderers complete their revolutions about Jupiter, and of their alterations as observed more precisely later on we shall give a description here.

Raymond J. Seeger. *Galileo Galilei: His Life and His Works*. (Oxford: Pergamon, 1966). 247–48, 250, 253–54, 255.

1. What invention is Galileo describing in this passage? _____

2. What two kinds of lenses were included in Galileo's instrument? _____

3. How does Galileo describe the moon's surface? _____

   _____

4. What planet did Galileo find with his instrument? On what day did he find it? _____

5. What did he find around the planet, and how did he describe them? What would we call these today? (The earth has one.) _____

   _____

   _____

6. What two planets does Galileo mention as revolving around the sun? _____

Name _____

Matching

Place the correct letter in the blank.

_F_ 1. Louis XIV

_D_ 2. Hippocrates

_C_ 3. Euclid

_G_ 4. Roger Bacon

_H_ 5. Oliver Cromwell

_E_ 6. Glorious Revolution

_I_ 7. English Bill of Rights

_A_ 8. Eratosthenes

_B_ 9. Copernicus

_J_ 10. Edward Jenner

A. Circumference of the earth
B. Earth revolves around the sun
C. Father of Geometry
D. Father of Medicine
E. William and Mary
F. King of France
G. Optics and astronomy
H. Protectorate
I. Set limits on royal power
J. Smallpox vaccination

A. Built large telescope	F. Human anatomy
B. Christian chemist	G. Human body is made of chemicals
C. Demands that religion be excluded	H. Predicted orbits of comets
D. Experience is the source of knowledge	I. Reason is the source of knowledge
E. Father of Modern Chemistry	J. Ruler of Russia

_F_ 11. Antoine Lavoisier

_I_ 12. Rationalism

_C_ 13. Secularism

_D_ 14. Empiricism

_B_ 15. Robert Boyle

_G_ 16. Paracelsus

_F_ 17. Andreas Vesalius

_H_ 18. Edmond Halley

_A_ 19. Sir William Herschel

_J_ 20. Catherine the Great

Name _____

Chapter Review
Completion

Underline the word or phrase that correctly completes the statement.

1. The (<u>Dutch</u>/French) developed an economic empire without the aid of a centralized monarchy.

2. The (Spanish/<u>English</u>) have been ruled by kings of German descent.

3. The (<u>Spanish</u>/English) took the lead in exploring and expanding their empire.

4. (Lavoisier/<u>Paracelsus</u>) believed that the body is made mostly of chemicals and should be treated with chemicals.

5. The vaccine to prevent the spread of smallpox was first developed by (Lavoisier/<u>Jenner</u>).

6. King James II was a strong supporter of the (<u>Roman</u>/Protestant) Church.

7. Catherine the Great continued the development of a strong monarchy in (<u>Russia</u>/England).

8. Hippocrates was known as the Father of (Chemistry/<u>Medicine</u>).

9. (Descartes/<u>Locke</u>) insisted that observation, not human reason, is the source of truth.

10. (<u>Lavoisier</u>/Paracelsus) became known as the Father of Modern Chemistry.

11. (Cromwell/<u>Galileo</u>) used a telescope to confirm that the earth revolved around the sun.

12. (Robert Boyle/<u>William Harvey</u>) studied the human circulatory system.

13. (<u>Louis XIV</u>/Charles II) became the model of an absolute monarch.

14. (<u>Eratosthenes</u>/Paracelsus) was the first person to determine lines of latitude and longitude.

15. (<u>Spinoza</u>/Descartes) doubted anything in Scripture that he thought was contrary to reason.

Matching

Write the correct letter in the blank.

__E__ 16. Society free from religion

__D__ 17. Human reason is the way to reach truth.

__C__ 18. Government system under Cromwell

__B__ 19. Truth is found through experience.

__A__ 20. Seventeenth and eighteenth centuries in Europe

A. Age of Reason
B. Empiricism
C. Protectorate
D. Rationalism
E. Secularism

Name _____

John G. Paton

Answer the questions below based on the following excerpts from John G. Paton's writings.

. . . [Once,] when Natives in large numbers were assembled at my house, a man furiously rushed on me with his axe; but a Kaserumini Chief snatched a spade with which I had been working, and dexterously [skillfully] defended me from instant death. Life in such circumstances led me to cling very near to the Lord Jesus; I knew not, for one brief hour, when or how attack might be made; and yet, with my trembling hand clasped in the hand once nailed on Calvary, and now swaying the scepter of the Universe, calmness and peace and resignation abode in my soul.

Next day, a wild Chief followed me about for four hours with his loaded musket, and, though [the gun was] often directed towards me, God restrained his hand. I spoke kindly to him, and attended to my work as if he had not been there, fully persuaded that my God had placed me there, and would protect me till my allotted task was finished. Looking up in unceasing prayer to our dear Lord Jesus, I left all in His hands, and felt immortal till my work was done. Trials and hairbreadth [narrow] escapes strengthened my faith, and seemed only to nerve me for more to follow; and they did tread swiftly upon each other's heels. Without that abiding consciousness of the presence and power of my dear Lord and Saviour, nothing else in all the world could have preserved me from losing my reason and perishing miserably. . . .

One evening, I awoke three times to hear a Chief and his men trying to force the door of my house. Though armed with muskets, they had some sense of doing wrong, and were wholesomely afraid of a little retriever dog which had often stood betwixt me and death. God restrained them again; and next morning the report went all round the Harbour, that those who tried to shoot me were "smitten weak with fear," and that shooting would not do. A plan was therefore [made] to [burn] the premises, and club us if we attempted to escape. But our Aneityumese Teacher heard of it, and God helped us to frustrate their designs.

John G. Paton. *John G. Paton, Missionary to the New Hebrides: An Autobiography Edited by His Brother.* Ed. James Paton (New York: Fleming H. Revell, 1907). 191–93.

1. What trials does Paton mention at the beginning of the passage? <u>A native attacked</u> <u>him with an axe, and a wild cheif followed him with a</u> <u>loaded musket.</u>

2. How did Paton respond to the trials? <u>He depended on God, remembered</u> <u>God's promises, and became more aware of the Lord's "presence</u> <u>and power."</u>

3. What animal scared a chief and his men who were trying to force their way into Paton's house? _____ <u>"a little retriever dog."</u>

Namuri, one of my Aneityumese Teachers, was placed at our nearest village. There he had built a house for himself and his wife, and there he led amongst the Heathen a pure and humble Christian life. Almost every morning, he came and reported on the state of affairs to me. Without books or a school, he yet instructed the Natives in Divine things, conducted the Worship, and taught them much by his good example. His influence was increasing, when one morning a Sacred Man threw at him the kawas, or killing stone, a deadly weapon, like a scythe stone in shape and thickness, usually round but sometimes angular, and from eighteen to twenty inches long. . . . The Priest [then] sprang upon him with his club and with savage yells. [Namuri] evaded, yet also received, many blows; and, rushing out of their hands, actually reached the Mission House, bleeding, fainting, and pursued by howling murderers. I had been anxiously expecting him, and hearing the noise I ran out with all possible speed.

On seeing me, he sank down by a tree, and cried,—

"Missi, Missi, quick! and escape for your life! They are coming to kill you; they say, they must kill us all to-day, and they have begun with me; for they hate Jehovah and the Worship!"

I hastened to the good Teacher where he lay; I bound up, washed, and dressed his wounds; and God, by the mystery of His own working, kept the infuriated Tannese watching at bay. . . . In three or four weeks, he so far recovered by careful nursing that he was able to walk about again. . . .

One morning during worship, when the good Teacher knelt in prayer, the same savage Priest sprang upon him with his great club and left him for dead, wounded and bleeding and unconscious. The people fled[,] . . . afraid of being mixed up with the murder. The Teacher, recovering a little, crawled to the Mission House, and reached it about mid-day in a dying condition. . . .

To him, Jesus was all and in all; and there were no bands in his death. He passed from us, in the assured hope of entering into the Glory of his Lord. Humble though he may appear in the world's esteem, I knew that a great man had fallen there in the service of Christ, and that he would take rank in the glorious Army of the Martyrs.

John G. Paton. *John G. Paton, Missionary to the New Hebrides: An Autobiography Edited by His Brother*. Ed. James Paton (New York: Fleming H. Revell, 1907). 193–96.

4. Why was Namuri attacked by a priest? _becouse he taught the people how to worship Jehovah._

5. What did the priest do to Namuri? _He threw a "killing stone", beat him, and later wounded him so severely that he died._

6. Why did the people flee when their teacher was hurt? _they did not want to be "mixed up with the murder"_

7. To what place did Namuri flee both times? _to the mission home where Paton was living._

Name _____

James Chalmers

Answer the questions below based on the following excerpts from Chalmers's writings.

During the last nine years I have seen much of Teava [a native pastor], and learned to admire the man. He lived much in prayer, and in the study of God's Word. At prayer-meetings he was always first there, coming at least half an hour before any one else, so that he might have time to pray and receive a blessing for himself and others before the service began. He was never absent from the deacons' Saturday afternoon prayer-meeting. He was always ready to speak to the church, ever pointing the members to Christ, and warning them against the many evils to which they are exposed. From his long, true, and earnest life he was able to speak to them as only very few could. He spoke very plainly, not at all mincing matters when occasion required. He had great regard for the *Pilgrim's Progress*, and his delight was to have me sit with him and go over a part of Christian's journey to Mount Zion, the heavenly Jerusalem.

From his position in the island he was able to speak faithfully to the chiefs. . . . For five weeks before his death he was unable to attend the services in church, but he welcomed any who could spend a short time with him in prayer in his own house. He told me some days before he died that he was just waiting on; he knew the Master had sent for him. He said he was done with all below, and looked only for Christ's presence. Not in what he had done did he trust, but in the Cross of Christ alone. On March 16 he asked for a little food. It was given him, but he could not eat it; he got up and walked a very short distance in the house, when he said, "I think the messenger has come to fetch me; I shall die." His wife and another woman laid him down on his mat, when he quietly passed away.

What a change! In his youth he was a heathen, had fought with, and had captured men and cooked and helped to eat them. In his manhood he was converted to Christ, became a true soldier of the Cross, and led many to the Saviour. In his death he trusted alone to Christ, conquered death in Christ, and went up to hear Him say, "Well done, good and faithful servant, enter thou into the joy of thy Lord."

Richard Lovett. *James Chalmers: His Autobiography and Letters*. (New York: Fleming H. Revell, 1902). 114–15.

1. How did Teava demonstrate his godliness? _____

_____

2. What book written by John Bunyan did Chalmers read with Teava? _____

3. How does Chalmers describe Teava's reaction to death? _____

_____

4. What was Teava like before his conversion? _____

In 1876 Mr. Royle retired to Sydney. For nearly forty years he and his good wife had laboured on Aitutaki, and only once during all that time had he been away from the island. I [suspect] the missionaries of the past thought more of their work than the missionaries of the present day. The latter seem to come out for ten years, even if they can stand the work so long, and the years and the months are counted, and often the furlough time is longed for. In 1863, Mr. Royle was induced to leave Aitutaki and pay Sydney a visit. On the way the *John Williams* [a ship] was wrecked on Danger Island (Pukapuka), and Mr. Royle always afterwards spoke of this as a punishment that befell him for daring to leave his work! When the vessel was nearly on the reef, and all had taken to the boats, Mr. Royle was seen seated calmly on a chair on the [deck]. The mate, Mr. Turpie, who was just getting over the side of the vessel, being the last to leave, noticing him, said, "Mr. Royle, why are not you in one of the boats?" "I must wait orders." "Well, be quick and get out of [the ship]." I know of only one other missionary who stayed so long at work without change, and he laboured for forty years without a break. . . . He knew the native language much better than any native, and was more conversant with the past of the Samoans than any single Samoan.

Lovett, Richard. *James Chalmers: His Autobiography and Letters*. (New York: Fleming H. Revell, 1902). 118.

5. In what Australian town did Mr. Royle decide to retire? _____

6. On what island in the Pacific did he evangelize the native peoples? How long did he work there?

   _____

7. What event happened during Mr. Royle's trip to Sydney? Why did he think this happened? _____

   _____

   _____

Name _____

James Cook's Journal

Answer the questions at the end based on the following excerpts from Cook's journal.

Friday, June 22nd, 1770. Some of the people were sent to shoot pigeons, and at their return reported that they had seen an animal as large as a greyhound, of a slender make, a mouse colour, and extremely swift.

June 23rd. This day almost everybody had seen the animal which the pigeon-shooters had brought an account of the day before.

June 24th. As I was walking this morning at a little distance from the ship, I saw myself one of the animals which had been so often described. It was of a light mouse colour, and in size and shape very much resembled a greyhound; it had a long tail also, which it carried like a greyhound; and I should have taken it for a wild dog if, instead of running, it had not leapt like a hare or deer. Its legs were said to be very slender, and the print of its foot to be like that of a goat; but where I saw it the grass was so high that the legs were concealed, and the ground was too hard to receive the track. Mr. Banks also had an imperfect view of this animal, and was of [the opinion] that its species was hitherto unknown.

July 8th. In a walk of many miles some of our men saw four animals of the same kind, two of which Mr. Banks' greyhound fairly chased, but they threw him out at a great distance by leaping over the long thick grass, which prevented his running. These animals were observed not to run upon four legs, but to bound or hop forward upon two.

July 14th. Mr. Gore, who went out this day with his gun, had the good fortune to kill one of the animals which had been so much the subject of our speculation. In form it is most like the jerboa [a small jumping rodent that lives in the desert], which it also resembles in its motion, but it greatly differs in size, the jerboa not being larger than a common rat, and this animal, when full grown, being as big as a sheep; this individual was a young one, much under its full growth, weighing only thirty-eight pounds.

The head, neck, and shoulders are very small in proportion to the other parts of the body; the tail is nearly as long as the body, thick near the body, and tapering towards the other end; the fore-legs of this individual were only eight inches long, and the hind-legs two-and-twenty. Its progress is by successive leaps or hops, of a great length, in an erect posture; the fore-legs are kept bent close to the breast, and seemed to be of use only for digging. The skin is covered with a short fur of a dark mouse or gray colour, excepting the head and ears, which bear a slight resemblance to those of a hare.

This animal is called by the natives Kangaroo.

The next day our kangaroo was dressed for dinner, and proved most excellent meat. On the 27th Mr. Gore shot a kangaroo which weighed eighty-four pounds. Upon examination, however, we found that this animal was not at its full growth. . . . We dressed it for dinner the next day; but, to our great disappointment, we found it had a much worse flavour than that we had eaten before.

James Cook and C. G. Cash. *The Life and Voyages of Captain James Cook: Selections with Introductions and Notes.* (London: Blackie and Son, n.d.). 46–48.

1. What animal did Cook and his crew find? How does Cook describe this animal? Kangaroo; large as a greyhound

2. What did this animal do that kept Cook from calling it a wild dog? instead of running leaped like a rabbit.

3. What were the sizes of the animals that Cook and his crew were able to capture? 38 and 84

4. To what already-known animals does Cook compare this unknown animal? _greyhound, hare_
deer, goat, jribou, and sheep

Hitherto we had safely navigated this dangerous coast, where the sea in all parts conceals shoals that suddenly project from the shore, and rocks that rise abruptly like a pyramid from the bottom, for an extent of two-and-twenty degrees of latitude, more than 1300 miles; and therefore hitherto none of the names that distinguish the . . . parts of the country that we saw are memorials of distress; but here we became acquainted with misfortune, and we therefore called the point which we had just seen farthest to the northward Cape Tribulation.

This Cape lies in latitude 16° 6' south, and longitude 145° 21' east. We steered along the shore N. by W. at the distance of between three and four leagues, having from fourteen to twelve and ten fathom water. On the night of Sunday, June 10th, 1770, a few minutes before eleven, the water shallowed at once from twenty to seventeen fathom, and before the lead could be cast again the ship struck and remained immovable, except by the heaving of the surge that beat her against the crags of the rock upon which she lay. In a few moments everybody was upon the deck, with countenances which sufficiently expressed the horrors of our situation.

We had stood off the shore three hours and a half with a pleasant breeze, and therefore knew that we could not be very near it; and we had . . . much reason to conclude that we were upon a rock of coral, which is more fatal than any other, because the points of it are sharp, and every part of the surface is so rough as to grind away whatever is rubbed against it even with the gentlest motion. . . . The men were so far impressed with a sense of their situation that not an oath was heard among them, the habit of profaneness, however strong, being instantly subdued by the dread of incurring guilt when death seemed to be so near.

James Cook, and C. G. Cash. *The Life and Voyages of Captain James Cook: Selections with Introductions and Notes.* (London: Blackie and Son, n.d.). 48–52.

5. What did Cook name the place where he was almost shipwrecked? _Cape Tribulation_

6. Upon what was the ship stuck? Why was this especially dangerous for the ship? _coral_
_____

7. Why were the sailors not swearing as they normally did? _did not want to die_
guilty.

Name _____

Pacific Exploration

Write the correct letter in the blank.

N 1. Dutch captain that sailed in search of a mythical unknown southern land

L 2. Islands discovered by Alvaro de Mendaña

J 3. Took command of the ships after the death of Mendaña

C 4. Carried passengers who were mostly convicts

I 5. Islands that lie between the Hawaiian Islands, Easter Island, and New Zealand

B 6. Musical instrument made from eucalyptus wood

K 7. Site of a failed Spanish settlement in the Pacific where many died of fever

A 8. Native people of Australia

M 9. Landing place of first Australian settlement

E 10. Game that contained elements of football and soccer

H 11. Missionary to the New Hebrides

G 12. Home of the Maoris

D 13. Norwegian explorer that proved it was possible to travel from Peru to the Pacific Islands

O 14. Australian colony named after the queen of England

F 15. Name of the land claimed by the Dutch East India Company

A. Aborigines
B. didgeridoo
C. First Fleet
D. Thor Heyerdahl
E. Marn Grook
F. New Holland
G. New Zealand
H. John Paton
I. Polynesia
J. Pedro Quirós
K. Santa Cruz
L. Solomon Islands
M. Sydney Cove
N. Abel Tasman
O. Victoria

Name _____

Chapter Review

Underline the word or phrase that makes the statement correct.

1. The First Fleet sailed to (Hawaii/<u>Australia</u>).

2. (<u>Cook's</u>/Bougainville's) ship was almost sunk when it grounded on the Great Barrier Reef.

3. (Polynesia/<u>Micronesia</u>) means "small islands."

4. Australia is about the size of the (<u>United States</u>/Soviet Union).

5. The didgeridoo is a (<u>musical instrument</u>/crude hut).

6. Thor Heyerdahl sailed on the (First Fleet/<u>Kon Tiki</u>) expedition.

7. Alvaro de Mendaña explored for (<u>Peru</u>/England).

8. Captain James Cook died on the (<u>Hawaiian</u>/Solomon) Islands.

9. Louis Bougainville colonized (Australia/<u>Tahiti</u>) for France.

10. (<u>Gregory Blaxland</u>/James Chalmers) discovered a passage through the Great Dividing Range.

11. (Arthur Phillip/<u>James Chalmers</u>) served as a missionary to Papua New Guinea.

12. The (Tasmanians/<u>Maoris</u>) are native peoples who live in New Zealand.

13. Captain Cook fed his crew (tomatoes/<u>sauerkraut</u>) to help prevent scurvy.

14. (<u>Canberra</u>/Sydney) is the capital of Australia.

15. Abel Tasman sailed for (France/<u>the Netherlands</u>).

16. Spanish exploration ended due to a lack of (<u>funds</u>/captains).

17. Spanish explorers named the (Mendaña/<u>Marquesas</u>) islands after the viceroy of Peru.

18. Abel Tasman discovered the island of (<u>Tasmania</u>/South Australia).

19. (<u>Arthur Phillip</u>/Bougainville) served as Australia's first governor.

20. (<u>Commonwealth of Australia</u>/New Zealand) is composed of six states including Queensland and New South Wales.

Name _____

Encounter with a Lion

Answer the questions below based on the following excerpts from Pierre du Jarric's account.

When the summer had come to an end, the King [Akbar] set out on his return journey to Lahor. He had desired . . . Xauier [a Catholic missionary] and his companion to travel with him; but the latter, anxious to avoid the commotion of the court, asked and obtained permission to go on before. On their journey they suffered much from cold and hunger, as well as from the badness of the road; for they had to go by rough paths which were often so narrow that there was room for only a single horseman. They were obliged, therefore, to travel very slowly and to stop frequently. Moreover, the elephant which carried their goods had great difficulty in climbing the mountains. Sometimes, feeling insecure on its feet, owing to the load which it carried, it supported itself with its trunk, making it serve the purpose of a staff.

At length, on the 13th of November, after many hardships, they arrived at Lahor, from whence they had set out on the 15th of May of the same year, 1597. The people of the town exhibited towards the [priest] and his companion a more friendly attitude than was their [usual practice]. It had previously been their practice to throw stones at them, and offer them other insults; but on this occasion they displayed neither incivility nor disrespect. The King and the Prince [Salim] arrived some days later, having lost on their way many horses and elephants, and several of their attendants. The Prince, too, had been in great danger of his life. One day, mounted on a female elephant without tusks, he went in pursuit of lions, and in the course of the chase, [encountered] some lion [cubs]. As these were but half grown, the elephant had no difficulty in killing them with her trunk. The next moment, however, the lioness their mother appeared, and in her rage would have hurled herself upon the Prince, had he not pierced her with an arrow as she was in the act of springing. But the wound was not [fatal], and the infuriated animal still strove to reach him who had struck her, to rend him with her claws and teeth. Again the Prince discharged his [gun], piercing her through and through a second time; but the savage beast was not [killed]; and [provoked] to even greater fury, she sprang upon the elephant, and so nearly reached the Prince that he was splashed with the foam from her mouth. Seeing himself in such danger, he grasped his [gun] like a club, and with the [handle] dealt the lioness so severe a blow on the head, that she fell to the ground stunned. A soldier then came up and killed her with his sword; but not before she had avenged herself on her last assailant, whom she tore severely with her claws. Perhaps it was our Saviour's will to save the Prince from this danger in order that the [Catholic] Church might increase, and many souls win salvation, when he came to the throne.

Pierre du Jarric. *Akbar and the Jesuits: An Account of the Jesuit Missions to the Court of Akbar.* Trans. Ç. H. Payne. (New York: Harper and Brothers, 1926). 78–80.

1. What dangers did Xauier and his companion experience in their travels? _____

_____

2. What animal attacked Prince Salim? _____

3. What did Salim do to protect himself? _____

4. According to Pierre du Jarric, why did God save Salim from danger? _____

_____

Name _____

Matching

Write the correct letter in the blank. Answers may be used more than once.

___F___ 1. Mongol rule in China

_____ 2. Developed long, complex plays

_____ 3. Destroyed the Byzantine Empire

_____ 4. Shah Ismail I

_____ 5. Built the Imperial City in China

_____ 6. Babur

_____ 7. Seized power in China during the seventeenth century

_____ 8. Painted landscapes and perfected porcelain

_____ 9. Abbas

_____ 10. Restored the Grand Canal

_____ 11. Developed a two-dimensional form of government

_____ 12. Zheng He

_____ 13. Anatolia

_____ 14. Seized power in China during the fourteenth century

_____ 15. Protected by the British East India Company

_____ 16. Mehmet II

_____ 17. Welcomed Jews who were expelled from Europe

_____ 18. Akbar

_____ 19. Istanbul

_____ 20. Taizu

A. Manchu dynasty
B. Ming dynasty
C. Mughal dynasty
D. Ottoman Empire
E. Safavid Empire
F. Yuan dynasty

Name _____

Chapter Review

Underline the word or phrase that makes the statement correct.

1. The Chinese perfected the production of (linen/porcelain).

2. (India/China) referred to itself as the Middle Kingdom.

3. (Babur/Ismail) founded the Safavid dynasty.

4. (Akbar/Babur) was the most effective Mughal ruler.

5. The (Ottomans/Ming) built a strong empire that endured for six centuries.

6. (Babur/Ismail) was a descendant of Chinggis Khan and Tamerlane.

7. Zheng He sailed on behalf of (India/China).

8. (Manchuria/India) lies north of China.

9. The (Ming/Manchu) dynasty reconstructed the Grand Canal.

10. The Ottomans were among the first to use (long bows/cannons) in battle.

11. The Safavid Empire followed the (Shiite/Sunni) interpretation of Islam.

12. (Turkish/Afghan) forces overthrew the Safavid Empire in 1722.

13. The (Ottoman/Manchu) Empire viewed merchants and artisans as essential to the empire's economic success.

14. The Ottomans destroyed the Byzantine Empire and changed the name of its capital city to (Constantinople/Istanbul).

15. The Ottoman Empire was initially dominated by (Turks/Mongols).

16. (Chengzu/Taizu) founded the Ming dynasty.

17. Painting (landscapes/portraits) was a popular form of art during the Ming dynasty.

18. The Ottomans took the city of Constantinople in the year (1437/1453).

19. (Mehmet II/Akbar) came to power in the Ottoman Empire and made the conquest of Constantinople his goal.

20. (Chengzu/Abbas) became the third emperor in the Ming dynasty.

Name _____

The Three Estates of France

Write the correct letter(s) in the blank. Answers will be used more than once, and an item might have more than one answer.

A. First Estate   B. Second Estate   C. Third Estate

_A_ 1. Clergy

_B_ 2. Nobility

_C_ 3. Merchants

_C_ 4. City laborers

_C_ 5. Rural laborers

_C_ 6. Twenty-four million members

_A_ 7. One hundred twenty thousand members

_B_ 8. Three hundred fifty thousand members

_A_ 9. Controlled vast land estates in France and owned valuable properties in the cities

_B_ 10. Owned about 20 percent of the land in France

_A_ 11. Only about half a percent of the French population

_C_ 12. Bore the heaviest tax burden in France

_C_ 13. Had little opportunity for economic growth

_A, B_ 14. Exempt from most taxes in France

_C_ 15. Required to perform feudal obligations

_C_ 16. Included the middle class

_C_ 17. Forced to pay fees to use mills, wine presses, and bakeries

_C_ 18. Formed the National Assembly and signed the Tennis Court Oath

_C_ 19. Signed the Declaration of the Rights of Man

_A, B_ 20. Received preference when Louis XVI convened the Estates-General

The Battle of Waterloo

Answer the questions at the end based on the following excerpts from the work of Captain R. H. Gronow, a British officer.

[June 18, 1815]

On the morning of the 18th the sun shone most gloriously, and so clear was the atmosphere that we could see the long, imposing lines of the enemy most distinctly. Immediately in front of the division to which I belonged, and, I should imagine, about half a mile from us, were posted cavalry and artillery; and to the right and left the French had already engaged us, attacking Huguemont and La Haye Sainte. We heard incessantly the measured boom of artillery, accompanied by the incessant rattling echoes of musketry.

The whole of the British infantry not actually engaged were at that time formed into squares; and as you looked along our lines, it seemed as if we formed a continuous wall of human beings. I recollect distinctly being able to see Bonaparte and his staff; and some of my brother officers using the glass [telescope], exclaimed, "There he is on his white horse."

I should not forget to state that when the enemy's artillery began to [fire] on us, we had orders to lie down, when we could hear the shot and shell whistling around us, killing and wounding great numbers; then again we were ordered on our knees to receive cavalry. The French artillery—which consisted of three hundred guns, though we did not muster more than half that number—committed terrible havoc during the early part of the battle, whilst we were acting on the defensive. . . .

About four P.M. the enemy's artillery in front of us ceased firing all of a sudden, and we saw large masses of cavalry advance: not a man present who survived could have forgotten in [later] life the awful grandeur of that charge. You [perceived] at a distance what appeared to be an overwhelming, long moving line, which, ever advancing, glittered like a stormy wave of the sea when it catches the sunlight. On they came until they got near enough, whilst the very earth seemed to vibrate beneath the thundering tramp of the mounted host. One might suppose that nothing could have resisted the shock of this terrible moving mass. They were the famous cuirassiers, almost all old soldiers, who had distinguished themselves on most of the battlefields of Europe. In an almost incredibly short period they were within twenty yards of us, shouting 'Vive l'Empereur!' [When the] word of command, "Prepare to receive cavalry," had been given, every man in the front ranks knelt, and a wall bristling with steel, held together by steady hands, presented itself to the infuriated cuirassiers. . . .

The charge of the French cavalry was gallantly executed; but our well-directed fire brought men and horses down, and ere long the utmost confusion arose in their ranks. The officers were exceedingly brave, and by their gestures and fearless bearing did all in their power to encourage their men to form again and renew the attack. . . .

It was about five o'clock on that memorable day, that we suddenly received orders to retire behind an elevation. . . . The enemy's artillery had come up [together] within a hundred yards of us. By the time they began to discharge their guns, however, we were lying down behind the rising ground, and protected by the ridge before referred to.

The enemy's cavalry was in the rear of their artillery, in order to be ready to protect it if attacked; but no attempt was made on our part to do so. After they had pounded away at us for about half an hour, they deployed, and up came the whole mass of the Imperial infantry of the Guard, led on by the Emperor in person. We had now before us probably about 20,000 of the best soldiers in France, the heroes of many memorable victories; we saw the bearskin caps rising higher and higher as they ascended the ridge of ground which separated us, and advanced nearer and nearer to our lines.

It was at this moment [that] the Duke of Wellington gave his famous order for our bayonet charge, as he rode along the line: these are the precise words he made use of—"Guards, get up and charge!" We were instantly on our legs, and after so many hours of inaction and irritation at maintaining a purely defensive attitude [position]—all the time suffering the loss of comrades and friends—the spirit which animated officers and men may easily be imagined. After firing a volley as soon as the enemy were within shot, we rushed on with fixed bayonets, and that hearty hurrah peculiar to British soldiers.

Joseph Grego. *The Reminiscences and Recollections of Captain Gronow: Being Anecdotes of the Camp, Court, Club, and Society, 1810–1860.* Vol. 1 (London: John C. Nimmo, 1900). 2 vols. 68–70, 73–74.

1. Whom could the British officers see through a telescope? _____

2. How does Gronow describe the French cavalry charge? _____

    _____

    _____

3. How many French soldiers composed the French Imperial infantry of the Guard? _____

4. Who personally led the French Imperial infantry of the Guard? _____

5. Which British officer gave orders for the bayonet charge? _____

Name _____

Europe

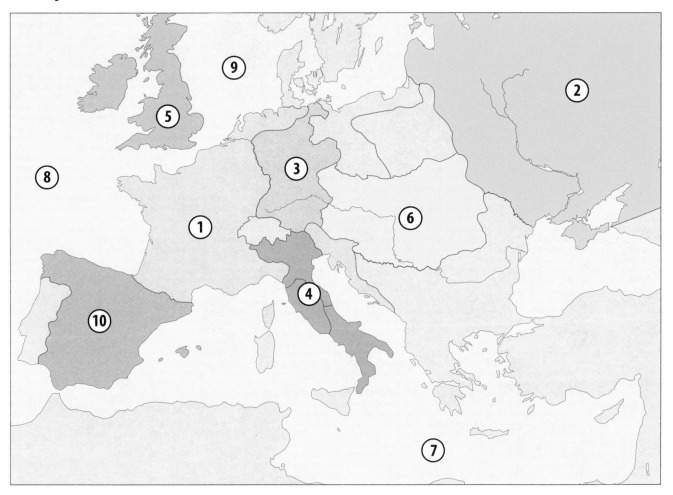

Locate the following on the map and write the number in the blank beside each term.

_8_ 1. Atlantic Ocean

_6_ 2. Austrian Empire

_5_ 3. Britain

_1_ 4. France

_3_ 5. Germany

_4_ 6. Italy

_7_ 7. Mediterranean Sea

_9_ 8. North Sea

_2_ 9. Russia

_10_ 10. Spain

Name _____

The Five Ws

Good reporters attempt to answer five basic questions: Who? What? Where? When? Why?
Using the Answer Bank, list the facts that a good newspaper should include in these reports.

Answer Bank		
People of Europe	Greece, Belgium, Poland, and Hungary	1866–71 and 1859–71
June 18, 1815	A decisive battle where the Prussian and British armies confronted Napoleon and his armies	For political, religious, and economic freedom
The French people	Repelling invaders	Unification within these nations
To expand German territory and a result of the drive toward nationalism	1800s	Britain and Prussia saw the need to stop Napoleon's expansion and policies
The political and financial collapse of France	Waterloo	Uprisings
1775–83	Napoleon Bonaparte	Germany and Italy
Revolt against their leaders and governments	A growing sense of nationalism started by the French	The American colonists
After the Estates-General assembled	In the American colonies	
Otto von Bismarck and Camillo di Cavour	France	

The French Revolution

Who? _The French People_

What? _Uprisings_

Where? _France_

When? _After the Estates-General Assembled_

Why? _The political and financial collapse of France_

American War for Independence

Who? _The American People_

What? _Repelling invaders_

Where? _In the American colonies_

When? _1775-83_

Why? _For political, religious, and economic freedom_

Fall of the French Dictator

Who? Napoleon Bonaparte

What? A decisive battle where the Prussian and British armies confronted Napoleon and his armies.

Where? Waterloo

When? June 15, 1815

Why? Britain and Prussia saw the need to stop Napoleon's expansion and policies

Nationalist Revolutions

Who? People of Europe

What? Revolts against their leaders and governments

Where? Greece, Belgium, Poland, and Hungary

When? 1800's

Why? A growing sense of nationalism started by the French.

Unification Movements

Who? Otto von Bismark and Camillo di Cavour

What? Unification within these nations

Where? Germany and Italy

When? 1866-71 and 1859-71

Why? To expand German territory and as a result of the drive toward nationalism.

Name _____

Chapter Review
Completion

Underline the word or phrase that correctly completes the statement.

1. The First Estate was composed of (merchants/clergy).

2. (France/Germany) endured the Reign of Terror in the eighteenth century.

3. (France/Germany) struggled to achieve unification.

4. France was predominately a (Protestant/Catholic) nation.

5. The Tennis Court Oath was taken in (France/Germany).

6. Napoleon was forced to retreat and leave most of his army in (Russia/Germany).

7. Count Camillo di Cavour became the prime minister of (England/Sardinia).

8. Marie Antoinette became the queen of (France/England).

9. (Garibaldi/Mazzini) was an Italian nationalist who formed the group Young Italy.

10. Napoleon was finally defeated at (Leipzig/Waterloo) in 1815.

11. Eastern Poland came under the domination of (Russian/Austrian) forces after the Congress of Vienna.

12. (Napoleon/Bismarck) became the First Consul of France.

13. The Belgians revolted and gained their independence from (the Netherlands/Austria).

14. The Zollverein was an economic union that played a role in the unification of (Italy/Germany).

15. Voltaire was an Enlightenment philosopher from (England/France).

Matching

Write the correct letter in the blank.

__B__ 16. Formed the army of the "Red Shirts"

__D__ 17. King of a united Italy

__E__ 18. King of Prussia during the unification period

__A__ 19. Chancellor of Prussia

__C__ 20. In power when France had a political and financial collapse

A. Otto von Bismarck
B. Giuseppi Garibaldi
C. Louis XVI
D. Victor Emmanuel II
E. Wilhelm I

Name _____

Edison, the Inventor

Answer the questions at the end based on the following excerpts from Edison's writings.

I never allow myself to become discouraged under any circumstances. I recall that after we had conducted thousands of experiments on a certain project without solving the problem, one of my associates . . . expressed discouragement and disgust over our having failed "to find out anything." I cheerily assured him that we *had* learned something. For we had learned for a certainty that the thing couldn't be done that way, and that we would have to try some other way. We sometimes learn a lot from our failures if we have put into the effort the best thought and work we are capable of. . . .

Deafness has done many good things for the world. In my own case it has been responsible, I think, for the perfection of the phonograph; and it had something to do with the development of the telephone into usable form. When Bell first worked out his telephone idea I tried it and the sound which came in through the instrument was so weak I couldn't hear it. I started to develop it and kept on until the sounds were audible to me. I sold my improvement, the carbon transmitter, to the Western Union and they sold it to Bell. It made the telephone successful. If I had not been deaf it is possible and even probable that this improvement would not have been made. The telephone as we now know it might have been delayed if a deaf electrician had not undertaken the job of making it a practical thing.

The phonograph never would have been what it now is and for a long time has been if I had not been deaf. Being deaf, my knowledge of sounds had been developed till it was extensive and I knew that I was not [getting overtones] and no one else was getting overtones. Others working in the same field did not realize this imperfection, because they were not deaf. Deafness, pure and simple, was responsible for the experimentation which perfected the machine. It took me twenty years to make a perfect record of piano music because it is full of overtones. I now can do it—just because I'm deaf.

My deafness has been a definite advantage in my business, too, in more ways than one. The fact that I do not rely on verbal agreements and reports is one reason for this. There would be a chance that I might not hear them perfectly. So I have everything set down in black and white. That has saved me certain difficulties which I might have had if I had been acute of hearing. My deafness never has prevented me from making money in a single instance. It has helped me many times. It has been an asset to me always.

Even in my courtship my deafness was a help. In the first place it excused me for getting quite a little nearer to her than I would have dared to if I hadn't had to be quite close in order to hear what she said. If something had not overcome my natural bashfulness I might have been too faint of heart to win. And after things were actually going nicely, I found hearing unnecessary.

My later courtship was carried on by telegraph. I taught the lady of my heart the Morse code, and when she could both send and receive we got along much better than we could have with spoken words by tapping our remarks to one another on our hands. Presently I asked her thus, in Morse code, if she would marry me. The word "Yes" is an easy one to send by telegraphic signals, and she sent it. If she had been obliged to speak it she might have found it harder. Nobody knew anything about many of our conversations on a long drive in the White Mountains. If we had spoken words, others would have heard them. We could use pet names without the least embarrassment, although there were three other people in the carriage. We still use the telegraphic code at times. When we go to hear a spoken play she keeps her hand upon my knee and telegraphs the words the actors use so that I know something about the drama though I hear nothing of the [dialogue].

Thomas Alva Edison. *The Diary and Sundry Observations of Thomas Alva Edison*. Ed. Dagobert D. Runes. (New York: Philosophical Library, 1948). 43, 53–55.

1. How did Edison avoid becoming discouraged? _____

2. What disability helped him improve two inventions? _____

_____

3. How did he turn his disability into an advantage in his business dealings? _____

_____

4. How did Edison communicate with his bride-to-be? _____

_____

5. How did Edison understand the drama of a spoken play with the help of his wife? _____

_____

Name _____

The Wright Brothers

Answer the questions at the end based on the following excerpts from the Wright brothers' account.

We began our active experiments . . . in October, 1900, at Kitty Hawk, North Carolina. Our machine was designed to be flown as a kite, with a man on board, in winds from 15 to 20 miles an hour. But, upon trial, it was found that much stronger winds were required to lift it. Suitable winds not being plentiful, we found it necessary, in order to test the new balancing system, to fly the machine as a kite without a man on board, operating the levers through cords from the ground. This did not give [us] the practice anticipated, but it inspired confidence in the new system of balance.

In the summer of 1901 we became personally acquainted with Mr. [Octave] Chanute. When he learned that we were interested in flying as a sport, and not with any expectation of recovering the money we were expending on it, he gave us much encouragement. At our invitation, he spent several weeks with us at our camp at Kill Devil Hill, four miles south of Kitty Hawk, during our experiments of that and the two succeeding years. He also witnessed one flight of the power machine near Dayton, Ohio, in October, 1904.

The machine of 1901 was built with the shape of surface used by Lilienthal, curved from front to rear like the segment of a parabola, with a curvature 1/12 the depth of its cord; but to make doubly sure that it would have sufficient lifting capacity when flown as a kite in 15 or 20-mile winds, we increased the [plane's] area from 165 square feet, used in 1900, to 308 square feet—a size much larger than Lilienthal, Pilcher, or Chanute had deemed safe. Upon trial, however, the lifting capacity again fell very far short of calculation, so that the idea of [getting] practice while flying [the plane] as a kite had to be abandoned. Mr. Chanute, who witnessed the experiments, told us that the trouble was not due to poor construction of the machine. We saw only one other explanation—that the tables of air-pressures in general use were incorrect.

We then turned to gliding—coasting downhill on the air—as the only method of getting the desired practice in balancing a machine. After a few minutes' practice we were able to make glides of over 300 feet, and in a few days were safely operating in 27-mile winds. In these experiments we met with several unexpected phenomena. We found that, contrary to the teachings of the books, the center of pressure on a curved surface traveled backward when the surface was inclined, at small angles, more and more edgewise to the wind. We also discovered that in free flight, when the wing on one side of the machine was presented to the wind at a greater angle than the one on the other side, the wing with the greater angle descended, and the machine turned in a direction just the reverse of what we were led to expect when flying the machine as a kite. The larger angle gave more resistance to forward motion, and reduced the speed of the wing on that side. The decrease in speed more than counterbalanced the effect of the larger angle. The addition of a fixed vertical vane in the rear increased the trouble, and made the machine absolutely dangerous. It was some time before a remedy was discovered. This consisted of movable rudders working in conjunction with the twisting of the wings. The details of this arrangement are given in specifications published several years ago.

The Early History of the Airplane by Orville and Wilbur Wright. Public Domain.

1. Where did Orville and Wilbur Wright start actively experimenting with airplanes? _____

_____

2. What was the size of the plane they used in 1901? _____

3. How far were the Wrights able to fly the airplane by gliding? _____

4. How many miles per hour were the wind gusts during their experiments? _____

In September and October, 1902, nearly 1,000 gliding flights were made, several of which covered distances of over 600 feet. Some, made against a wind of 36 miles an hour, gave proof of the effectiveness of the devices for control [steering]. With this machine, in the autumn of 1903, we made a number of flights in which we remained in the air for over a minute, often soaring for a considerable time in one spot, without any descent at all. Little wonder that our unscientific assistant should think the only thing needed to keep it indefinitely in the air would be a coat of feathers to make it light!

The Early History of the Airplane by Orville and Wilbur Wright. Public Domain.

5. What did the flights made in winds of 36 miles per hour allow the Wright brothers to demonstrate?

   _____

6. According to their assistant, what would enable the plane to remain in the air indefinitely? _____

   _____

Name _____

"Thoughts upon Slavery"—John Wesley

Answer the questions at the end based on the following excerpts from Wesley's writings.

That part of Africa whence the Negroes are brought, commonly known by the name of Guinea, extends along the coast, in the whole, between three and four thousand miles. From the river Senegal, seventeen degrees north of the line, to Cape Sierra-Leone, it contains seven hundred miles. Thence it runs eastward about fifteen hundred miles, including the Grain Coast, the Ivory Coast, the Gold Coast, and the Slave Coast, with the large kingdom of Benin. From thence it runs southward, about twelve hundred miles, and contains the kingdoms of Congo and Angola. . . .

Upon the whole . . . the Negroes who inhabit the coast of Africa, from the river Senegal to the southern bounds of Angola, are so far from being the stupid, senseless, brutish, lazy barbarians, the fierce, cruel, perfidious [deceitful] savages they have been described, that, on the contrary, they are . . . remarkably sensible, considering the few advantages they have for improving their understanding; as industrious to the highest degree, perhaps more so than any other natives of so warm a climate; as fair, just, and honest in all their dealings, unless where white men have taught them to be otherwise; and as far more mild, friendly, and kind to strangers, than any of our forefathers were. *Our forefathers!* Where shall we find at this day, among the fair-faced natives of Europe, a nation generally practicing the justice, mercy, and truth, which are found among these poor Africans? . . . [W]e may leave England and France, to seek genuine honesty in Benin, Congo, or Angola. . . .

Is there a God? You know there is. Is he a just God? Then there must be a state of retribution; a state wherein the just God will reward every man according to his works. Then what reward will he render to you? O think [quickly]! before you drop into eternity! Think now, "He shall have judgment without mercy that showed no mercy."

Are you a man? Then you should have an human heart. But have you indeed? What is your heart made of? Is there no such principle as compassion there? Do you never feel another's pain? Have you no sympathy, no sense of human woe, no pity for the miserable? When you saw the [tearful] eyes, the heaving breasts, or the bleeding sides and tortured limbs of your fellow-creatures, [were] you a stone, or a brute? Did you look upon them with the eyes of a tiger? When you squeezed the agonizing creatures down in the ship, or when you threw their poor mangled remains into the sea, had you no relenting? Did not one tear drop from your eye, one sigh escape from your breast? Do you feel no [remorse] now? If you do not, you must go on, till the measure of your iniquities is full. Then will the great God deal with you as you have dealt with them, and require all their blood at your hands. And at "that day it shall be more tolerable for Sodom and Gomorrah than for you!" But if your heart does relent, though in a small degree, know it is a call from the God of love. And "to-day, if you will hear his voice, harden not your heart." To-day resolve, God being your helper, to escape for your life. . . . Immediately quit the horrid [slave] trade: At all events, be an honest man.

John Wesley. "Thoughts upon Slavery." *The Works of John Wesley*. 3rd ed. Vol. 11. (Grand Rapids, MI: Baker Books, 2007). 14 Vols. 61, 64–65, 76–77.

1. From what African kingdoms and regions were the slaves brought? _____

   _____

2. What two countries does Wesley describe as not having genuine honesty when compared with the Africans?

   _____

3. What will God do to those who fail to show mercy to others? _____

4. What should be the proper human attitude toward slaves? _____

5. According to Wesley, what should the British people do about the slave trade in order to be honest men?

_____

Liberty is the right of every human creature, as soon as he breathes the vital air; and no human law can deprive him of that right which he derives from the law of nature.

If, therefore, you have any regard to justice, (to say nothing of mercy, nor the revealed law of God,) render unto all their due. Give liberty to whom liberty is due, that is, to every child of man, to every partaker of human nature. Let none serve you but by his own act and deed, by his own voluntary choice. Away with all whips, all chains, all [force]! Be gentle toward all men; and see that you . . . do unto every one as you would he should do unto you. . . .

O thou God of love, thou who art loving to every man, and whose mercy is over all thy works; thou who art the Father of the spirits of all flesh, and who art rich in mercy unto all; thou who hast mingled of one blood all the nations upon earth; have compassion upon these outcasts of men, who are trodden down as dung upon the earth! Arise, and help these that have no helper, whose blood is spilt upon the ground like water! Are not these also the work of thine own hands, the purchase of thy Son's blood? Stir them up to cry unto thee in the land of their captivity; and let their complaint come up before thee; let it enter into thy ears! Make even those that lead them away captive . . . pity them, and turn their captivity as the rivers in the south. O burst thou all their chains in sunder; more especially the chains of their sins! Thou Saviour of all, make them free, that they may be free indeed!

John Wesley. "Thoughts upon Slavery." *The Works of John Wesley*. 3rd ed. Vol. 11. (Grand Rapids, MI: Baker Books, 2007). 14 Vols. 79.

6. What is the right of every human creature? _____

7. What characteristics of God are mentioned in Wesley's prayer? _____

_____

8. What two kinds of freedom does Wesley pray for the Africans to receive? _____

_____

Name _____

Letter from John Wesley to William Wilberforce

Answer the questions below based on the following letter by Wesley.

LONDON, February 26, 1791.

DEAR SIR,

UNLESS the divine power has raised you up to be [one man against the world], I see not how you can go through your glorious enterprise, in opposing that [wickedness], which is the scandal of religion, of England, and of human nature. Unless God has raised you up for this very thing [of ending slavery], you will be worn out by the opposition of men and devils. But, "if God be for you, who can be against you?" Are all of them together stronger than God? O "be not weary in well doing!" Go on, in the name of God and in the power of his might, till even American slavery (the vilest that ever saw the sun) shall vanish away before it.

Reading this morning a tract, [written] by a poor African, I was particularly struck by that circumstance,—that a man who has a black skin, being wronged or outraged by a white man, can have no [justice]; it being a law, in all our colonies, that the oath of a black against a white goes for nothing. What [injustice] is this!

That He who has guided you from your youth up, may continue to strengthen you in this and all things, is the prayer of [John Wesley.]

John Wesley. "Letter to a Friend." *The Works of John Wesley*. 3rd ed. Vol. 13. (Grand Rapids, MI: Baker Books, 2007). 14 Vols. 153.

1. With what scriptural phrases does Wesley encourage Wilberforce? _____

   _____

2. According to Wesley, what country practiced "the vilest" form of slavery? _England_____

3. What had Wesley recently read that described the injustices suffered by slaves? _____

   _____

4. What did Wesley pray for Wilberforce? _____

   _____

Name _____

"On the Horrors of the Slave Trade"

Answer the questions below based on the following speech delivered by William Wilberforce.

[Delivered in the House of Commons on May 12, 1789]

In opening, concerning the nature of the slave trade, I need only observe that it is found by experience to be just such as every man who uses his reason would infallibly conclude it to be. For my own part, so clearly am I convinced of the mischiefs inseparable from it, that I should hardly want any further evidence than my own mind would [provide], by the most simple deductions. Facts, however, are now laid before the House. A report has been made by his majesty's privy council, which, I trust, every gentleman has read, and which [confirms] the slave trade to be just as [evil as] we know. What should we suppose must naturally be the consequence of our carrying on a slave trade with Africa? With a country vast in its extent, not utterly barbarous, but civilized in a very small degree? Does any one suppose a slave trade would help their civilization? Is it not plain that she must suffer from it; that civilization must be [stopped]; that her barbarous manners must be made more barbarous; and that the happiness of her millions of inhabitants must be [injured by] her [slave trade] with Britain? Does not every one see that a slave trade carried on around her coasts must carry violence and desolation to her very center? That in a continent just emerging from barbarism, if a trade in [slavery] is established, if her men are all converted into goods, and become commodities that can be [bought and sold], [then] they must be subject to [abuse] just as goods are; and this, too, at a period of civilization, when there is no protecting legislature to defend this, their only sort of property, in the same manner as the rights of property are maintained by the legislature of every civilized country. . . .

Sir, the nature and . . . circumstances of this trade are now laid open to us; we can no longer plead ignorance, we can not evade it; it is now an object placed before us, we can not pass it; . . . we can not turn aside so as to avoid seeing it; for it is brought now so directly before our eyes that this House must decide . . . the [rightness] of the grounds and principles of their decision.

http://en.wikisource.org/wiki/On_the_Horrors_of_the_Slave_Trade

1. Before what assembly did Wilberforce present this speech? _____

2. According to Wilberforce, what effects would the slave trade have on Africa? _____

   _____

   _____

3. According to Wilberforce, what could Africa have achieved if there had been no slave trade? _____

   _____

4. According to Wilberforce, what could the British no longer plead regarding the African slave trade?

   _____

Name _____

Chapter Review

Matching

Write the correct letter in each blank.

__J__	1. Jethro Tull	A. Cotton gin
__N__	2. Andrew Meikle	B. Entrepreneur
__A__	3. Eli Whitney	C. Flying shuttle
__I__	4. Cyrus McCormick	D. Former slave; abolitionist
__M__	5. John Fowler	E. Former slave ship captain; abolitionist
__L__	6. James Watt	F. Great Awakening
__C__	7. John Kay	G. Methodist leader
__K__	8. James Hargreaves	H. Newspaper editor
__B__	9. Richard Arkwright	I. Reaping machine
__G__	10. John Wesley	J. Seed drill
__F__	11. George Whitefield	K. Spinning jenny
__E__	12. John Newton	L. Steam engine
__O__	13. William Wilberforce	M. Steam tractor
__H__	14. William Lloyd Garrison	N. Threshing machine
__D__	15. Frederick Douglass	O. Worked in Parliament to end slavery

Completion

Underline the word or phrase that makes the statement correct.

16. (Crop rotation/Crop tilling) helped farmers increase production.

17. The growth of (cottage industries/factories) resulted in many moving to the city.

18. The (1833 Factory Act/Ten Hour Bill) placed limits on child labor and required some schooling.

19. The (Factory Revolution/Industrial Revolution) began in Great Britain.

20. The (patent/capital) provided inventors with protection for their inventions.

Name _____

The Dreyfus Affair

Answer the questions at the end based on the following fictionalized account of the Dreyfus Affair.

I can still remember that cold day in January 1894. Having just turned fourteen, I had recently found a job as an apprentice at the town bakery. Rushing to my first day of work, I heard a commotion in the town square. As a crowd grew and the noise swelled, my urgency to get to the bakery was overruled, and I stopped to find out the cause of such a stir in our town. I still remember my shock at the scene. Soldiers forcefully restrained an artillery captain while he frantically shouted to them and the gathered citizens.

"I am innocent! Vive la France! I am an innocent man!"

Eager to get a better view, I pushed my way through the crowd until I stood just a few feet from the captain and those who held him tightly. Soon an officer stepped forward and proceeded to read a charge of treason! As we stood in stunned surprise, a sergeant advanced and ripped the shiny buttons from the captain's uniform, tossing them into the half-frozen mud. I remember flinching at the sound of shredding fabric when the sergeant yanked the stripes and other military emblems from the captain's coat and trousers. In a final gesture of contempt, the sergeant took the captain's dress sword, snapped it over his knee, and cast the broken weapon aside.

The man, identified as a Captain Dreyfus, continued to declare his innocence, but the crowd soon drowned out his cries with insults and taunts. I must confess that I joined in this chorus and called him names that I now am ashamed to repeat. But, I thought, he must be guilty! Surely the army would not condemn an innocent man.

To complete the captain's humiliation, the soldiers force-marched him around the square to endure the continued outcries of the onlookers. Then they tied his hands and carried him off in a prison wagon.

By this time, I had recollected how angry the baker would be over my late appearance. Dreading a box on the ears, I quickly scurried off to his shop. But upon arriving, I was relieved to find that, save for a sharp rebuke, all of his energy was bent toward finding out the details of the public spectacle I had just witnessed. I retold the story in true sensational fashion for a rapt audience of bakery workers and patrons.

But life continued on, and, hearing no more about the captain and being preoccupied with our own affairs, I and my neighbors soon forgot about him until one day late in the fall. Near closing time, a regular customer excitedly barged into the bakery to announce the conviction of Captain Dreyfus for treason! His sentence (recounted in an ominous tone) was captivity for life in the infamous prison at Devil's Island, French Guiana. I believe all of us, including me, shuddered to think of being sent to that place! We later heard that, even worse, the authorities had placed him in isolation in a small, cramped cell! I wondered how anyone could long survive such unbearable conditions.

Two years later, the baker moved me to the front of the shop to wait on patrons, giving me many more opportunities to catch the latest gossip. One day, a customer came in with astonishing news. Apparently, the military had discovered the real traitor, but had then covered up the evidence! No one seemed to know the details, but, now uncertain, I paused as memories of my own behavior that day rushed back to haunt me. I felt terrible for the things I had shouted with the crowd. Surely, I thought, the authorities will set the innocent captain free!

But three more years passed, and Captain Dreyfus continued to languish in prison. By this time, I was nearly twenty years old and still working at the bakery. One mild day at the tail end of summer, the doorbell jingled as one of our regulars entered. As I looked up to greet him, the excitement on his face stopped me. He had visited the bakery to tell us that Captain Dreyfus had finally gained his freedom! Oh, the relief we all felt! Such a thing had weighed heavily on my conscience. It was not until a few years later, though, that I learned the Captain was Jewish and that this was the main motivation behind the false accusations against him. I still wince at the memory of my disappointment and shame. To know that people in my country would commit such shameful acts against a man simply because of prejudice against his ancestry!

1. What crime was Alfred Dreyfus accused of committing? _____

2. What did Dreyfus shout to the soldiers and the crowd? _____

_____

3. What did the army do to humiliate him? _____

_____

4. After convicting him of committing treason, where did the French government send Dreyfus to serve his

sentence? _____

5. How many years was Dreyfus imprisoned before his release? _____

6. Why did the French government keep Dreyfus in prison even after he was proven innocent? _____

_____

Name _____

Hard Times

Answer the questions at the end based on the following excerpts from Charles Dickens's work.

[from Part I, ch. 11] The [factories] burst into illumination, before pale morning showed the monstrous serpents of smoke trailing themselves over Coketown. A clattering of clogs [shoes] upon the pavement; a rapid ringing of bells; and all the melancholy mad elephants, polished and oiled up for the day's monotony, were at their heavy exercise again.

Stephen bent over his loom, quiet, watchful, and steady. A special contrast, as every man was in the forest of looms where Stephen worked, to the crashing, smashing, tearing piece of mechanism at which he laboured. . . .

So many hundred Hands [workers] in this Mill; so many hundred horse Steam Power. . . .

The day grew strong, and showed itself outside, even against the flaming lights within. The lights were turned out, and the work went on. The rain fell, and the Smoke-serpents, submissive to the curse of all that tribe, trailed themselves upon the earth. In the waste-yard outside, the steam from the escape pipe, the litter of barrels and old iron, the shining heaps of coals, the ashes everywhere, were shrouded in a veil of mist and rain.

The work went on, until the noon-bell rang. More clattering upon the pavements. The looms, and wheels, and Hands all out of gear for an hour.

Stephen came out of the hot mill into the damp wind and cold wet streets, haggard and worn. He turned from his own class and his own quarter, taking nothing but a little bread as he walked along, towards the hill on which his principal employer lived, in a red house with black outside shutters, green inside blinds, a black street door, up two white steps, BOUNDERBY (in letters very like himself) upon a brazen plate, and a round brazen door-handle underneath it. . . .

[from Part II, ch. 1] The streets were hot and dusty on the summer day, and the sun was so bright that it even shone through the heavy vapour drooping over Coketown, and could not be looked at steadily. Stokers emerged from low underground doorways into factory yards, and sat on steps, and posts, and palings, wiping their swarthy [faces], and contemplating coals. The whole town seemed to be frying in oil. There was a stifling smell of hot oil everywhere. The steam-engines shone with it, the dresses of the Hands were soiled with it, the mills throughout their many stories oozed and trickled it. The atmosphere of those [factories] was like the breath of the simoom [desert wind]: and their inhabitants, wasting with heat, toiled languidly in the desert. But no temperature made the melancholy mad elephants more mad or more sane. Their wearisome heads went up and down at the same rate, in hot weather and cold, wet weather and dry, fair weather and foul. The measured motion of their shadows on the walls, was the substitute Coketown had to show for the shadows of rustling woods; while, for the summer hum of insects, it could offer, all the year round, from the dawn of Monday to the night of Saturday, the whirr of shafts and wheels.

Drowsily they whirred all through this sunny day, making the passenger more sleepy and more hot as he passed the humming walls of the mills. Sun-blinds, and sprinklings of water, a little cooled the main streets and the shops; but the mills, and the courts and alleys, baked at a fierce heat. Down upon the river that was black and thick with dye, some Coketown boys who were [playing]—a rare sight there—rowed a crazy boat, which made a spumous [foamy] track upon the water as it jogged along, while every dip of an oar stirred up vile smells. But the sun itself, however beneficent, generally, was less kind to Coketown than hard frost, and rarely looked intently into any of its closer regions without engendering more death than life.

Hard Times by Charles Dickens. Public Domain.

1. The mill in Dickens's story is located in what imaginary city? _____

2. To what animal does Dickens compare each large, polished, and oiled machine? _____

3. What term does Dickens use in the first paragraph to illustrate that factory work was very boring?

   _____

4. With what machine is Stephen working? _____

5. What powers the machines in this story? _____

Name _____

Charles Darwin

Answer the questions at the end based on the following excerpts from Darwin's autobiography.

. . . After I had two sessions in Edinburgh, my father perceived, or he heard from my sisters, that I did not like the thought of being a physician, so he proposed that I should become a clergyman [pastor]. He was very properly [set] against my turning into an idle sporting man, which then seemed my probable destination. I asked for some time to consider, as from what little I had heard or thought on the subject I had scruples about declaring my belief in all the dogmas of the Church of England; though otherwise I liked the thought of being a country clergyman. Accordingly I read with great care *Pearson on the Creed*, and a few other books on divinity; and as I did not then in the least doubt the strict and literal truth of every word in the Bible, I soon persuaded myself that our Creed must be fully accepted.

Considering how fiercely I have been attacked by the orthodox [Christians], it seems ludicrous that I once intended to be a clergyman. Nor was this intention and my father's wish ever formally given up, but died a natural death when, on leaving Cambridge, I joined the *Beagle* as naturalist. If the phrenologists [those who study the shape and bumps of a person's skull] are to be trusted, I was well fitted in one respect to be a clergyman. A few years ago the secretaries of a German psychological society asked me earnestly by letter for a photograph of myself; and some time afterwards I received the proceedings of one of the meetings, in which it seemed that the shape of my head had been the subject of a public discussion, and one of the speakers declared that I had the bump of reverence developed enough for ten priests.

As it was decided that I should be a clergyman, it was necessary that I should go to one of the English universities and take a degree; but as I had never opened a classical book since leaving school, I found to my dismay, that in the two intervening years I had actually forgotten, incredible as it may appear, almost everything which I had learnt, even to some few of the Greek letters. I did not therefore proceed to Cambridge at the usual time in October, but worked with a private tutor in Shrewsbury, and went to Cambridge after the Christmas vacation, early in 1828. I soon recovered my school standard of knowledge, and could translate easy Greek books, such as Homer and the Greek [New] Testament, with moderate facility [ease]. . . .

[*During the intervening years, Darwin sailed on the Beagle (1831–36), became the Secretary of the Geological Society, married Emma Wedgewood, and continued his study of geology and natural selection.*]

In September 1858 I set to work by the strong advice of Lyell and Hooker to prepare a volume on the transmutation of species, but was often interrupted by ill-health, and short visits to . . . [the medical] establishment at Moor Park. I [continued to write my manuscript] . . . and completed the volume. . . . It cost me thirteen months and ten days' hard labour. It was published under the title of the *Origin of Species*, in November 1859. Though considerably added to and corrected in the later editions, it has remained substantially the same book.

It is no doubt the chief work of my life. It was [immediately] highly successful. The first small edition of 1250 copies was sold on the day of publication, and a second edition of 3000 copies soon afterwards. Sixteen thousand copies have now (1876) been sold in England; and considering how stiff a book it is, this is a large sale. It has been translated into almost every European tongue, even into such languages as Spanish, Bohemian [Czech or Slovak], Polish, and Russian. . . . Even an essay in Hebrew has appeared on it, showing that the theory is contained in the Old Testament!

Charles Darwin: His Life Told in an Autobiographical Chapter, and in a Selected Series of His Published Letters (London: John Murray, 1908), 17, 41–42. (https://books.google.com/books?id=sMvTAAAAMAAJ&pg=PA17&lpg=PA17&dq=spent+two+sessions+in+Edinburgh,+my+father+perceived&source=bl&ots=eZwjP9932t&sig=3hLuJUwlo10Sv9syzA0N3v-2RwI&hl=en&sa=X&ei=yInTVLbiGo3yggShqlHYAg&ved=0CDMQ6AEwBQ#v=onepage&q=spent%20two%20sessions%20in%20Edinburgh%2C%20my%20father%20perceived&f=false)

1. When Charles Darwin decided that he did not want to be a doctor, what did he consider becoming?

   Clergyman

2. What was Darwin's view of the Bible early in his life? _he accepted it._

3. When Darwin was training to be a clergyman and went to school again, what language did he have to relearn?

   Greek

4. How did Darwin describe the *Origin of Species* in relation to his life's work? _____

   _____

5. How popular was this book when it was published? _____

   _____

6. An unnamed author wrote an essay in Hebrew about Darwin's book. What did the author of this essay claim about Darwin's theory? _____

Name _____

Crossword Puzzle

Across

1. Legislation that removed some power from the House of Lords in the English Parliament
4. No drinking of alcohol
5. Wrote about the negative aspects of the Industrial Revolution
6. Movement that sought universal manhood suffrage
9. Patented the telephone
11. Studied to be a pastor, but instead became a naturalist
12. Reaction to capitalism
14. Common ownership of property

Down

1. Heating liquids to slow the growth of microbes
2. Legislation that granted voting privileges to all male homeowners in Britain
3. Prime minister that doubled the number of men eligible to vote
7. Gave people the ability to send messages using a system of wires
8. Artistic style that pictures everyday life in realistic detail
10. Scottish scientist who studied physics and astronomy
13. Developed the code for the telegraph

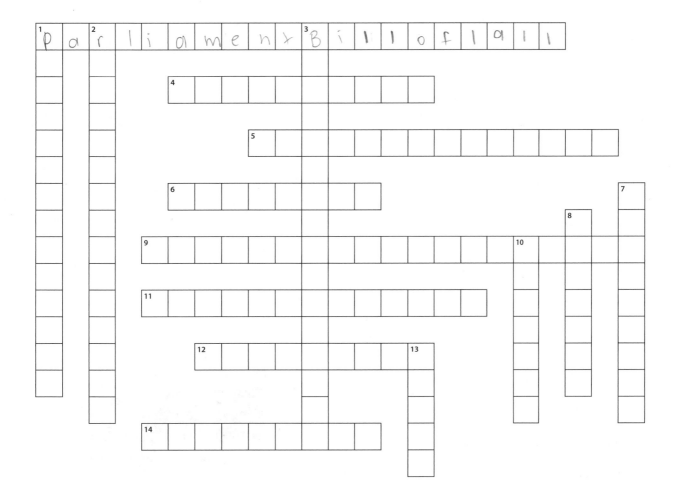

Name _____

Chapter Review
Matching I
Write the correct letter in the blank.

__C__ 1. Karl Marx

__H__ 2. Proletariat

__L__ 3. Suffrage

__B__ 4. Bourgeoisie

__J__ 5. Temperance movement

__I__ 6. Repeal of the Corn Laws

__G__ 7. Reform Bill of 1832

__N__ 8. William Gladstone

__M__ 9. Louis Napoleon Bonaparte

__F__ 10. Third Republic

__A__ 11. Richard Wagner

__D__ 12. French artillery captain who was humiliated

__K__ 13. Murder of Jews in Russia

__E__ 14. Romanticism

__O__ 15. Leo Tolstoy

A. Anti-Semitism
B. Capitalists (middle class)
C. Communist Manifesto
D. Alfred Dreyfus
E. Emphasized emotion
F. Forced the French emperor into exile
G. Granted suffrage to the middle class
H. Laborers
I. Lowered the cost of food
J. Opposed the manufacture or sale of alcohol
K. Pogrom
L. Privilege to vote
M. Second Republic
N. Stressed domestic reform
O. War and Peace

Matching II

__E__ 16. Steam engine

__B__ 17. Wright brothers

__D__ 18. Internal combustion engine

__A__ 19. Canada

__C__ 20. Mexico

A. British North America Act
B. Built the first successful airplane
C. Porfirio Diaz
D. Received its power from inside the engine
E. Received its power from outside the engine

Name _____

David Livingstone

Answer the questions below based on the following excerpts from Livingstone's writings.

. . . I have to offer only a simple account of a mission which, with respect to the objects [goals] proposed to be thereby accomplished, formed a noble contrast to some of the earlier expeditions to Eastern Africa. I believe that the information [my narrative] will give, respecting the people visited and the countries traversed, will not be materially [contradicted] by any future commonplace traveler like myself. . . . This account is written in the earnest hope that it may contribute to that information which will yet cause the great and fertile continent of Africa to be no longer kept . . . sealed, but made available as the scene of European enterprise, and will enable its people to take a place among the nations of the earth, thus securing the happiness and prosperity of tribes now sunk in barbarism or debased by slavery; and, above all, I cherish the hope that it may lead to the introduction of the blessings of the Gospel. . . .

The main object of the Zambesi Expedition, as our instructions from her majesty's government explicitly stated, was to extend the knowledge already attained of the geography and mineral and agricultural resources of Eastern and Central Africa—to improve our acquaintance with the inhabitants, and to [encourage] them to apply themselves to industrial pursuits and to the cultivation of their lands, [so that] . . . raw material [might] be exported to England in return for British manufactures; and it was hoped that, by encouraging the natives to occupy themselves in the development of the resources of the country, a considerable advance might be made toward the [ending] of the slave-trade. . . . The Expedition was sent in accordance with the settled policy of the English government. . . .

Our first object was to explore the Zambesi, its mouths and tributaries, with a view to their being used as highways for commerce and Christianity to pass into the vast interior of Africa.

David and Charles Livingstone. *Narrative of an Expedition to the Zambesi and its Tributaries; and of the Discovery of the Lakes Shirwa and Nyassa. 1858–1864.* (New York: Harper and Brothers, 1866). 2, 9, 14.

1. What reasons did Livingstone give for writing about his expedition? _____

_____

_____

2. To what European nation did Livingstone hope that Africa's raw materials could be sent? _____

3. What trade did Livingstone hope would end when Africa developed its natural resources? _____

4. What river did Livingstone hope would be a way for "commerce and Christianity" to enter Africa's interior?

_____

Both banks are dotted with hippopotamus traps over every track which these animals have made in going up out of the water to graze. The hippopotamus feeds on grass alone, and, where there is any danger, only at night. Its enormous lips act like a mowing machine, and form a path of short-cropped grass as it feeds. We never saw it eat aquatic [water] plants or reeds. The tusks seem weapons of both offense and defense. The hippopotamus trap consists of a beam five or six feet long, armed with a spear-head or hard-wood spike, covered with poison, and suspended to a forked pole by a cord, which, coming down to the path, is held by a catch, to be set free when the beast treads on it. Being wary [cautious] brutes, they are still very numerous. One got frightened by the ship as [the ship] was steaming close to the bank. In its eager hurry to escape it rushed on shore, and ran directly under a trap, when down came the heavy beam on its back, driving the poisoned spear-head a foot deep into its flesh. In its agony it plunged back into the river, to die in a few hours, and afterward furnished a feast for the natives. The poison on the spear-head does not affect the meat, except the part around the wound, and that is thrown away. In some places the descending beam is weighted with heavy stones, but here the hard heavy wood is sufficient.

David and Charles Livingstone. *Narrative of an Expedition to the Zambesi and its Tributaries; and of the Discovery of the Lakes Shirwa and Nyassa. 1858–1864*. (New York: Harper and Brothers, 1866). 106–7.

5. What animal did the natives catch and eat? _____

6. What scared the animal out of the river and into the trap? _____

7. How did the Africans catch this animal? _____

_____

Name _____

Through the Dark Continent

Answer the questions at the end based on the following excerpts from Henry M. Stanley's writings.

[1876,] Dec. 8.—On the 8th of December we moved down river to Unya-N'singé, another large town, a mile in length, on the north side of a creek, about thirty yards wide. On the south side, on the summit of bluffs 125 feet high, was a similar town called Kisui-cha-Uriko.

About four miles up the river from Unya-N'singé, the Lira river entered the Livingstone. At the mouth it was 300 yards wide and 30 feet deep, but two miles above it narrowed to 250 yards of deep and tolerably clear water. A hostile movement on the part of the natives, accompanied by fierce demonstrations on shore, compelled us, however, to [give up] the design of penetrating farther up, and to hurry back to camp at Unya-N'singé.

We had not been long there before we heard the war-horns sounding on the right bank, and about 4 P.M. we saw eight large canoes coming up river along the islands in midstream, and six along the left bank. On approaching the camp they formed in line of battle near a small grassy island about four hundred yards from us, and shouted to us to come and meet them in mid-river. Our interpreters were told to tell them that we had but one boat, and five canoes loaded with sick people; and that as we had not come for the purpose of fighting, we would not fight.

A jeering laugh greeted the announcement, and the next minute the fourteen canoes dashed towards us with wild yells. I [arranged] my people along the [river] banks, and waited. When they came within thirty yards, half of the men in each canoe began to shoot their poisoned arrows, while the other half continued to paddle in-shore. Just as they were about to land, the command to fire was given to about thirty muskets, and the savages fell back, retiring to the distance of about a hundred and fifty yards, whence they maintained the fight. Directing the people on shore to keep firing, I chose the boat's crew, including Tippu-Tib and Bwana Abdallah, and dashed out into mid-stream. The savages appeared to be delighted, for they yelled triumphantly as they came towards us; only for a short time, however, for we were now only some fifty yards from them and our guns were doing terrible execution. In about a minute the fight was over, and our wild foes were paddling down river; and we returned to our camp, glad that this first affair with the Wasongora Meno had terminated so quickly. Three of our people had been struck by arrows, but a timely application of caustic neutralized the poison, and, excepting swellings, nothing serious occurred.

Unya-N'singé is in south latitude 2° 49'. Nearly opposite it is Urangi, another series of small villages; while on the north bank of the Lira River, at the confluence, is the village of Uranja, and opposite to it is Kisui Kachamba. The town of Meginna is said to be about twenty miles south-east (magnetic) from Unya-N'singé. All this portion is reported to have been the scene of Muini Muhala's exploits.

Dec. 9, 10, 11—. . . [Our friends] had, it appeared, again gone astray, and had entered Ukusu, where they were again obliged to fight. Four had received grievous wounds, and one had been killed. Three Wanyamwezi, moreover, had died of small-pox en route from Ikondu.

This creek, like all the rest in the neighbourhood, was half-choked with . . . asparagus-like plants [that the Aborigines enclosed with logs of wood]. When the log-enclosed spaces are full, the plants are taken out, exposed to the sun until they are withered, dried, and then burnt. The ashes are collected in pots with punctured bottoms, and the pots [are] filled with water which is left to drip through into shallow basins. After the evaporation by fire of this liquid, a dark grey sediment of a nitrous flavour is left, which, re-cleansed, produces salt.

Henry M. Stanley. *Through the Dark Continent or, The Sources of the Nile Around the Great Lakes of Equatorial Africa and Down the Livingstone River to the Atlantic Ocean*. Vol. 2. (New York: Dover, 1988). 2 vols. 135–37. Reprint.

1. What event prevented Stanley's group from traveling farther up the river? _____

2. When the Africans challenged the Europeans to fight, what did the interpreter tell them? _____
_____

3. What weapon did the Africans use to attack Stanley's group? _____

4. What weapon did the members of Stanley's group use to defend themselves? _____

5. What did the explorers do to treat those who had been struck by poisoned arrows? _____
_____

6. According to Stanley, with what was the creek "half-choked"? _____

7. When these plants were processed by the natives, what was the final product? _____

Name _____

Imperialism in Africa 1914

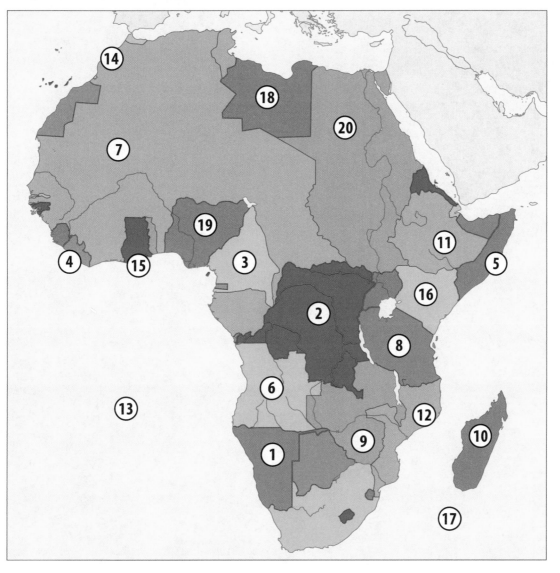

Locate the following on the map and write the number in the blank beside the term.

_11_ 1. Abyssinia	_7_ 8. French West Africa	_18_ 15. Libya
_6_ 2. Angola	_8_ 9. German East Africa	_10_ 16. Madagascar
_13_ 3. Atlantic Ocean	_1_ 10. German Southwest Africa	_14_ 17. Morocco
_2_ 4. Belgian Congo	_15_ 11. Gold Coast	_12_ 18. Mozambique
_16_ 5. British East Africa	_17_ 12. Indian Ocean	_19_ 19. Nigeria
_3_ 6. Cameroon	_5_ 13. Italian Somaliland	_9_ 20. Rhodesia
_20_ 7. Egypt	_4_ 14. Liberia	

Name _____

Abuses of Colonialism

Answer the questions at the end based on the following excerpts from the writings of Rev. Robert Bedinger, a missionary to Africa.

Cruelty.—"All the cruelties of Alva in the Lowlands, all the tortures of the Inquisition, all the savagery of the Spanish to the Caribs are as child's play compared with the deeds of the Belgians in the Congo."—Conan Doyle. This is a reference to the atrocities of the Leopoldian regime, happily past. But what can be said for the contempt in which the black man is held by the white? Why does the native still flee into the bush at the approach of the white man? In every way, the native is made to feel his inferiority. He resents being kicked about like a dog. Belgium is not alone in the guilt of cruel and inhuman treatment of natives. "What shall we say of the unjust and cruel wars of suppression in which practically every European power has engaged, of punitive expeditions which have been little better than massacres? The things Europe has done under this category are a disgrace to civilization."—Patton.

Taxation.—The native never stops to think of the benefits of the Government[,] and the fact that he resents the [requirement] of a tax only marks him as human. From his point of view, it is an oppressive measure to tax him for the privilege of living in his own country! Whether the tax be low or high it rankles in his bosom. It is obviously unjust to force lads of fourteen to pay taxes, as is done in the Congo. The tax in the Kasai is $1.20 per [year], the equivalent of one month's pay.

Limitation of Travel.—Although by nature a hunter or a trader, the native finds himself confined to a district and cannot go beyond its borders without a permit which is often hard to obtain. To be taxed is hard enough, but to be limited in travel makes him feel like a slave. In certain districts where forced labor is required, he is a slave. Industrial slavery is often as bad as the old form of slavery.

Diseases of [European] Civilization.—"The history of civilization in Africa may be traced by the diseases which spring up in its track." Rinderpest, tick-fever, east-coast fever—these are the cattle pests. To them must be added certain human ills, like tuberculosis, smallpox, and [other] diseases which are working . . . sad havoc. Tribal and family restraints have been broken down[,] and civilization offers no remedy. Certain tribes are more immoral than before the coming of the white man. In the face of such indictments, what is [European] civilization to say? . . .

The Liquor Problem.—This is an evil against which the natives make no protest. Yet no race is so quickly demoralized by strong drink as the black. Restrictive measures for its sale are enforced in certain quarters, but financial considerations stand in the way of its total prohibition. Holland, England, Germany, and the United States are the greatest sinners. "The British Board of Trade reports that during the year ending in April, 1916, there were imported into British West Africa 3,815,000 gallons of spirits [alcohol]. During 1914–15, from the port of Boston, there were shipped to the west coast of Africa 1,571,353 gallons of rum." To the credit of the Belgian Government, we gladly record that the sale of intoxicating [drinks] to the natives is strictly prohibited. It is unfortunate that the same law does not apply to the whites.

Industrial Centers.—Forty per cent of the world's output of gold comes from "The Rand," in South Africa. It has been estimated that . . . half a million blacks each year come under the influence of this one industrial center. The natives are recruited from every tribe south of the Zambezi. Some 300,000 are steadily employed at Johannesburg, which has been called, not without reason, "a university of crime." These natives are mostly young men from sixteen to twenty-five years old. At the mines they are [divided] in barracks or compounds, from 2,000 to 6,000 males in each. Those in the city naturally gravitate to the slums. Tribal and family restraints are removed. Some of the worst crooks and criminals of Europe and America descend to the lowest depths in order to [steal] from the native his hard earned cash. "The result is that we find natives [giving in] to drunkenness, gambling, murder, [and other sinful lifestyles]. To the vices of heathenism, the heathen are now adding those of [European] civilization."

Robert Dabney Bedinger. *Triumphs of the Gospel in the Belgian Congo.* (Richmond, VA: Presbyterian Committee of Publication, 1920). 184–86.

1–3. List three negative effects of European colonialism in Africa. _____

_____

4. What were Africans required to carry in order to travel? _____

5. Name one human disease that European colonists spread to Africa. _____

_____

6. How much alcohol did the British bring into Africa from 1915 to 1916? _____

7. According to Bedinger, what city in South Africa was noted for its sinfulness and was called "a university of crime"? _____

Name _____

Chapter Review
Completion
Underline the word or phrase that correctly completes the statement.

1. The (German/<u>British</u>) navy helped end the African slave trade.

2. (Egypt/<u>Ethiopia</u>) developed a modern army to defend itself against European invasion.

3. Warfare among African tribes generally (<u>decreased</u>/increased) after the slave trade ended.

4. Robert Moffat's daughter married (<u>David Livingstone</u>/Henry Stanley).

5. Oxford University gave (<u>Samuel Crowther</u>/John Horton) an honorary degree for his work in Africa.

6. (Olive/<u>Palm</u>) oil, the leading export of Africa, was used by industrial nations to lubricate machines.

7. European states pressured Africans to sign treaties during phase (<u>one</u>/two) of the Scramble for Africa.

8. (France/<u>Britain</u>) transported about three and one-half million slaves to the New World.

9. The (Horton/<u>Fante</u>) Confederation promoted self-rule and education for African males and females.

10. Menelik ruled (<u>Ethiopia</u>/Algeria) and thwarted Italian efforts to conquer his country.

11. (<u>Leopold</u>/Samori Ture) controlled the International African Association and abused the Africans in the region he colonized.

12. (Russia/<u>France</u>) relentlessly attacked Samori Ture's empire in West Africa.

13. (Henry Stanley/<u>Robert Moffat</u>) served as a missionary in South Africa for fifty-three years.

14. The African scholar (<u>John Africanus Horton</u>/Samuel Ajayi Crowther) disproved the claims that the black man was racially inferior.

15. The African ruler (<u>Macemba</u>/Samuel Ajayi Crowther) wrote a letter to the Germans and rejected their pressure to accept German domination.

Matching
Write the correct letter in the blank.

_A_ 16. Resulted in key agreements between Europeans

_E_ 17. African tribal language

_C_ 18. Built by Europeans in Africa

_D_ 19. African empire

_B_ 20. African economy

A. Berlin Conference
B. gathering-based
C. infrastructure
D. Wassoulou
E. Yoruba

Name _____

Slaughter of the Armenians

Answer the questions below based on the following excerpts from John Adger's writings.

In the year 1895, Messrs. G. P. Putnam's Sons, of New York, published a work entitled *The Armenian Crisis in Turkey, The Massacre of 1894, its Antecedents and Significance*, by Frederick Davis Greene, M. A., for several years a resident of Armenia. A portion of this volume consists of eighteen letters written from the interior of Armenia, before and during and immediately after the massacre. The author of this volume thus introduces them into his volume: "These letters were written by men who subjected themselves to personal danger by putting such statements on paper and sending them through the Turkish mails." . . .

It must be borne in mind that no writer was an eyewitness of the actual massacre; nor could he have been, inasmuch as the whole region was surrounded by a military [blockade] during the massacre, and for months after. The letters are largely based on the testimony of refugees from that region, or of Kurds and soldiers who participated in the butchery, and who had no hesitation in speaking about the affair in public or private until long after, when the [possibility] of a European investigation sealed their lips. Much of the evidence is, therefore, essentially first-hand, having been obtained from eye-witnesses by parties in the vicinity at the time, who are impartial, thoroughly experienced in sifting Oriental testimony, familiar with the Turkish and Armenian languages, and [completely trustworthy]. . . .

There is absolute [agreement] to this extent, that a gigantic and indescribably horrible massacre of Armenian men, women, and children did actually take place in the Sassoun and neighboring regions about September 1, 1894, . . . at the hands of Kurdish troops armed by the Sultan of Turkey, as well as [at the hands] of regular soldiers sent under orders from the same source. What those orders were will probably never [become known]. That they were [carried out] under the personal direction of high Turkish military officers is clear.

John B. Adger. *My Life and Times: 1810–1899*. (Richmond, VA: The Presbyterian Committee of Publication, 1899). 673–74.

1. According to Adger, what group of people was attacked? _____

2. How did the Ottoman attackers make it very difficult for anyone to be an eyewitness to the genocide?

_____

3. How does Adger describe the genocide? _____

4. What two groups of Ottomans were responsible for this incident? _____

To give the reader an adequate idea of these unquestionably [accurate] testimonies, I here [attach] extracts from Letter 6 . . . and Letter 9.

FROM LETTER No. 6.

"At first the [Kurds attacked], and the troops kept out of sight. The villagers put to the fight, and thinking they had only the [Kurds] to do with, repulsed them [drove them away] on several occasions. The [Kurds] were unwilling to do more unless the troops assisted. Some of the troops assumed [Kurdish] dress, and helped them in the fight with more success. Small companies of troops entered several villages, saying they had come to protect them as loyal subjects, and were quartered among the houses. In the night they arose and slew the sleeping villagers, man, woman, and child. . . .

No distinctions were made between persons or villages as to whether they were loyal and had paid their taxes or not. The orders were to make a clean sweep. A priest and some leading men from one village went out to meet an officer, taking in their hands their tax receipts, declaring their loyalty, and begging for mercy; but the village was surrounded, and all human beings put to the bayonet." . . .

FROM LETTER No. 9.

"The question arises," continues Frederick Davis Greene, "how did the missionaries feel, and how did they behave through all this period?" I answer with two or three statements as a sample of the whole.

The Rev. C. F. Gates, president of Euphrates College, Harpoot, wrote thus November 13th: "For three days we have looked death in the face hourly. We have passed by the mouth of the bottomless pit, and the flames came out against us, but not one in our company flinched or faltered. We simply trusted in the Lord and went on. . . . Threats abound, and the times are critical, but in all these things we are more than conquerors through him that loved us." . . .

The reader should bear in mind that these Moslem massacres of 1894–'97 are not the only ones recorded in the history of Turkey. Similar atrocities were visited upon the Greeks in 1822; upon the Nestorians in 1850; upon the Syrians in 1860; upon the Cretans in 1867; upon the Bulgarians in 1876; upon the Yezidees in 1892, and the Armenians in 1894. The spirit of Islam is still that of Mohammed, "The Koran or the Sword."

John B. Adger. *My Life and Times: 1810–1899*. (Richmond, VA: The Presbyterian Committee of Publication, 1899). 674–75, 678–79, 681.

5. What did the Armenians show to the attackers to prove their own loyalty? _____

6. To what religion did the attackers belong? What motto describes the spirit of this religion? _____

_____

Name _____

The Sepoy Mutiny

Answer the questions below based on the following excerpts from William Butler's writings.

The year in which I arrived in India saw the introduction of new arrangements for arming the Sepoy army. Instead of the old "Brown Bess," or regulation musket, with which they had hitherto fought the battles of the British, the rulers of India concluded to arm their Sepoys with the new Enfield rifle. For this weapon a [unique] cartridge had to be prepared, samples of which had been sent out from England to be manufactured at the arsenal of Dum Dum, eight miles from Calcutta. . . .

Then came the intense excitement about the "greased cartridges" for these guns, the purpose being, I suppose, to lubricate the bore of the rifle. It was given out that this grease was "a compound of hogs' lard and [cows'] fat." Only those who have lived among these people, and realized what a horror the [Muslim] has of the hog [as unclean], and what a reverence the Hindoo has for the cow, can appreciate the storm of excitement and frenzy this simple announcement caused through the whole Bengal army. . . .

It has never been definitely settled whether the charge as to the composition of the [grease] was correct or not. The Government did what it could to [ease] the excitement and fears of the Sepoys, even to the withdrawal of the obnoxious cartridges, offering the men the right to make them up themselves with such grease as was not offensive to them. But it was all too late; midnight meetings now began to be held and plans of resistance discussed, and immediate and open mutiny was proposed.

William Butler. *The Land of the Veda: Being Personal Reminiscences of India—Its People, Castes, Thugs, and Fakirs; Its Religions, Mythology, Principal Monuments, Palaces, and Mausoleums, Together with the Incidents of the Great Sepoy Rebellion.* (New York: Eaton and Mains, 1906). 223–24.

1. What new equipment did the British give to the Indian troops? _____

   _____

2. What material was supposedly used to grease the new cartridges? _____

   _____

3. Why were these greased cartridges offensive to the Muslims and Hindus? _____

   _____

. . . On Thursday, May 14, the commanding officer kindly sent his Adjutant [assisting officer] over to our house with a serious message. Not knowing what he . . . wanted, we engaged for nearly an hour in religious conversation. But I thought from his manner that he looked [worried]. With gentlemanly delicacy he was unwilling to mention his message before Mrs. Butler, lest it might injuriously affect her, as she was in circumstances where any shock was undesirable. He, accordingly, asked to see me alone, and then communicated the intelligence [message] of the mutiny at Meerut, stating that word had arrived from the Governor that the [mutiny] was spreading to Delhi and other places, and that fears were [rising] as to the intention of the Sepoys at Bareilly. Under those circumstances, the commanding officer felt it his duty to request that all ladies and children should be sent off quietly, but at *once*, to the hills, and also that he considered it prudent, from the [rumors] concerning us and our objects, that I also should accompany Mrs. B[utler] and the children, as he considered me in rather special danger in the event of a mutiny. . . . As soon as the Adjutant had gone, I communicated the message to Mrs. Butler. She received it with calmness, and we retired to our room to pray together for divine direction. . . .

. . . We were ready [to leave] when our bearers came at nine o'clock, and I went into my study once more. I looked at my books, etc., and the thought flashed across my mind that perhaps, after all my pains in collecting them, I should never see them again! I took up my Hindustanee Grammar, two volumes of manuscript Theological Lectures, a couple of works on India, my Passport, my Commission, and Letter of Instructions, with my Bible, Hymn Book, and a copy of the Discipline, and sorrowfully turned away, leaving the remainder to their fate. . . .

The rebels went to my house, and expressed great regret at not finding me. They are said to have declared they [especially] wanted me. They then destroyed our little place of worship, and burned my house with its contents. All was lost, save life and the grace of God; but the sympathy and prayers of our beloved Church were still our own, so the loss was not so great after all.

It would be [untrue] if I were to profess that I was unmoved at my loss. So far from it, I felt overwhelmed by it. Every thing was so complete and well arranged for my work. But all was destroyed, and some things gone that could never be restored. All my manuscripts; my library, (about one thousand volumes, the collection of my life, and which, perhaps, I loved too well,) so complete in its Methodistic and [doctrinal] and missionary departments; my globe, maps, microscope; our clothes, furniture, [small organ], buggy, stock of provisions—every thing, gone; and here we were, like shipwrecked mariners, grateful to have escaped with life. But we tried to say, "The Lord gave, and the Lord hath taken away; blessed be the name of the Lord." I had the [comfort] to know that my goods had been sacrificed for Christ's sake. . . .

William Butler. *The Land of the Veda: Being Personal Reminiscences of India—Its People, Castes, Thugs, and Fakirs; Its Religions, Mythology, Principal Monuments, Palaces, and Mausoleums, Together with the Incidents of the Great Sepoy Rebellion.* (New York: Eaton and Mains, 1906). 234, 237–38, 249–50.

4. What belongings did William Butler take with him when he fled the Sepoy attacks? _____

_____

_____

5. What did the Sepoys destroy? _____

6. What was Butler's reaction to his great loss? _____

_____

Name _____

The Goforths and the Boxer Rebellion

Answer the questions at the end based on the following excerpts from Rosalind Goforth's writings.

. . . I was seized with an overwhelming fear of what might be awaiting us. It was not the fear of *after* death, but of probable torture, that took such awful hold of me. I thought, "Can this be the Christian courage I have looked for?" I went by myself and prayed for victory, but no help came. Just then some one called us to a room for prayer before getting into our carts. Scarcely able to walk for trembling, and utterly ashamed that others should see my state of panic,—for such it undoubtedly was,—I managed to reach a bench beside which my husband stood. He drew from his pocket a little book, "Clarke's Scripture Promises," and read the verses his eye first fell upon. They were the following:

"The eternal God is thy refuge, and underneath are the everlasting arms: and he shall thrust out the enemy from before thee; and shall say, Destroy them."

"The God of Jacob is our refuge."

"Thou art my help and my deliverer; make no tarrying, O my God."

"I will strengthen thee; yea, I will help thee; yea, I will uphold thee with the right hand of my righteousness. . . . The Lord thy God will hold thy right hand, saying unto thee, Fear not; I will help thee." . . .

After prayer we all got on our carts, and one by one passed out into the densely crowded street. As we approached the city gate we could see that the road was black with crowds awaiting us. I had just remarked to my husband on how well we were getting through the crowds, when our carts passed through the gates. My husband turned pale as he pointed to a group of several hundred men, fully armed, awaiting us. They waited till all the carts had passed through the gate, then hurled down upon us a shower of stones, at the same time rushing forward and maiming or killing some of the animals. Mr. Goforth jumped down from our cart and cried to them, "Take everything, but don't kill." His only answer was a blow. The confusion that followed was so great it would be impossible to describe the escape of each one in detail. Each one later had his or her own testimony of that mighty and merciful deliverance. But I must give the details of Mr. Goforth's experience.

One man struck him a blow on the neck with a great sword wielded with two hands. "Somehow" the blunt edge of the sword struck his neck; the blow left a wide mark almost around his neck, but did no further harm. Had the sharp edge struck his neck he would certainly have been beheaded! . . .

Again he was felled to the ground, with a fearful sword cut, which entered the bone of the skull behind and almost cleft it in two. As he fell he seemed to hear distinctly a voice saying, "Fear not, they are praying for you." Rising from this blow, he was again struck down by a club. As he was falling almost unconscious to the ground he saw a horse coming at full speed toward him; when he became conscious again he found the horse had tripped and fallen (on level ground) so near that its tail almost touched him. The animal, kicking furiously, had served as a barrier between him and his assailants. While [Mr. Goforth was] dazed and not knowing what to do a man came up as if to strike, but whispered, "Leave the carts." By that time the onlookers began to rush forward to get the loot, but the attacking party felt the things were theirs, so desisted in their attack upon us in order to secure their booty.

A word as to myself and the children. Several fierce men with swords jumped on my cart. One struck at the baby, but I [blocked] the blow with a pillow, and the little fellow only received a slight scratch on the forehead. Then they dropped their swords and began tearing at our goods at the back of the cart. Heavy boxes were dragged over us, and everything was taken. Just then a dreadful looking man tried to reach us from the back of the cart with his sword, missing by an inch. I thought he would come to the front and continue his attack, but he did not. I had seen Mr. Goforth sink to the ground covered with blood twice, and had given him up for dead. Just then [my son] Paul, who had been in the last cart, jumped in, wild with delight at what he seemed to think was great fun, for he had run through the thick of the fight, dodging sword thrusts from all sides, and had succeeded in reaching me without a scratch. A moment later my husband came to the edge of the cart scarcely able to stand, saying, "Get down quickly; we must not delay in getting away." As I was getting down one man snatched away my hat, another my shoes; but we were allowed to go. . . .

We soon joined the rest of the party, and by six o'clock that evening we reached the large city of Nang Yang Fu. The city wall was black with people, and as we entered the gate the wild crowds crushed against our carts. Sometimes the animals staggered, and it seemed as if nothing could save the carts from being overturned. Every moment or two a brick or stone would be hurled against the carts, and that cry, "Kill, kill," which can never be forgotten when once heard, was shouted by perhaps hundreds of voices. Yet the Lord brought us through, and "no weapon prospered."

Rosalind Goforth. *How I Know God Answers Prayer: The Personal Testimony of One Life-Time* (Philadelphia: The Sunday School Times Company, 1921), 51–54, 58. (https://books.google.com/books?id=KTBFAAAAYAAJ&source=gbs_navlinks_s)

1. About what did Rosalind Goforth have an "overwhelming fear"? _____

2. With what scriptural truths did the Goforths comfort themselves during the Boxer Rebellion?

   _____

3. When Mr. Goforth first saw the Chinese attackers, what did he yell to protect himself and those with him?

   _____

4. How did the fallen horse actually protect him? _____

5. How did Rosalind Goforth protect her baby? _____

Name _____

Perry's Expedition to Japan

Answer the questions at the end based on the following excerpts.

From the beginning, the two [Japanese] princes had assumed an air of [stiff] formality which they [kept] during the whole interview, as they never spoke a word, and rose from their seats only at the entrance and exit of the Commodore, when they made a grave and formal bow. Yezaiman and his interpreters acted as masters of ceremony during the occasion. On entering, they took their positions at the upper end of the room, kneeling down beside a large lacquered box of scarlet color, supported by feet, gilt or of brass.

For some time after the Commodore and his suite had taken their seats there was a pause of some minutes, not a word being uttered on either side. Tatznoske, the principal interpreter, was the first to break silence, which he did by asking Mr. Portman, the Dutch interpreter, whether the letters were ready for delivery, and stating that the prince Toda was prepared to receive them; and that the scarlet box at the upper end of the room was prepared as the [place to receive] them. The Commodore, upon this being communicated to him, beckoned to the boys who stood in the lower hall to advance, when they immediately obeyed his summons and came forward, bearing the handsome boxes which contained the President's letter and other documents. . . .

Eva March Tappan, ed. *The World's Story: A History of the World in Story, Song and Art*, vol. 1: *China, Japan, and the Islands of the Pacific*, (Boston: Houghton Mifflin, 1914), 435–36.

[Letter from President Filmore to the emperor of Japan, November 13, 1852]
GREAT AND GOOD FRIEND: I send you this public letter by Commodore Matthew C. Perry, an officer of the highest rank in the navy of the United States, and commander of the squadron now visiting your imperial majesty's dominions.

I have directed Commodore Perry to assure your imperial majesty that I [have] the kindest feelings toward your majesty's person and government, and that I have no other object in sending him to Japan but to propose to your imperial majesty that the United States and Japan should live in friendship and have commercial intercourse with each other.

The Constitution and laws of the United States forbid all interference with the religious or political concerns of other nations. I have particularly charged Commodore Perry to abstain from every act which could possibly disturb the tranquility of your imperial majesty's dominions.

The United States of America reach from ocean to ocean, and our Territory of Oregon and State of California lie directly opposite to the dominions of your imperial majesty. Our steamships can go from California to Japan in eighteen days.

Our great State of California produces about sixty millions of dollars in gold every year, besides silver, quicksilver [mercury], precious stones, and many other valuable articles. Japan is also a rich and fertile country, and produces many very valuable articles. Your imperial majesty's subjects are skilled in many of the arts. I am desirous that our two countries should trade with each other, for the benefit both of Japan and the United States. . . .
Millard Fillmore.
By the President

Millard Fillmore Papers, vol. 1. Ed. Frank H. Severance (Buffalo, NY: Buffalo Historical Society, 1907). http://archive.org/stream /millardfillmore01fillgoog/millardfillmore01fillgoog_djvu.txt.

1. Why did Commodore Perry come to Japan and give the Japanese emperor this letter? _____

_____

2. According to President Fillmore, what did the Constitution and laws of the United States forbid?

_____

3. In 1852, how long did it take for a steamship to travel from America's west coast to Japan? _____

4. What did President Fillmore say that California produced in abundance? _____

_____

5. According to President Fillmore, who would benefit from Japan's participating in foreign trade?

_____

Name _____

Spread of Imperialism

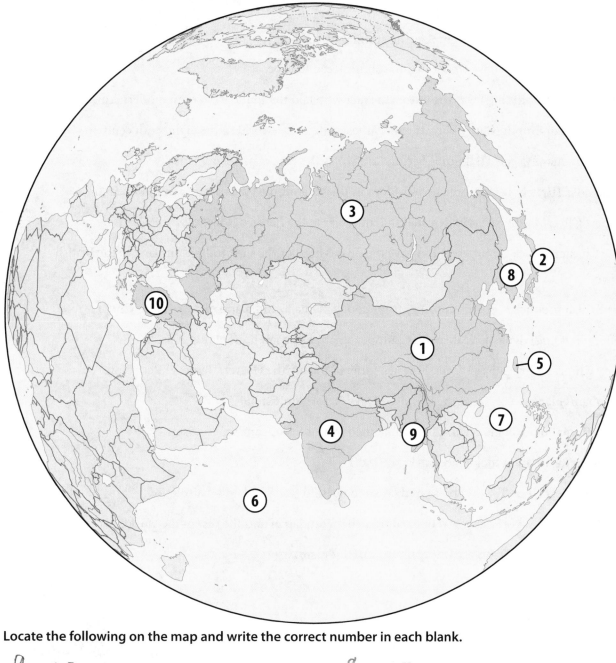

Locate the following on the map and write the correct number in each blank.

_9_ 1. Burma

_1_ 2. China

_4_ 3. India

_6_ 4. Indian Ocean

_2_ 5. Japan

_8_ 6. Korea

_10_ 7. Ottoman Empire

_3_ 8. Russia

_7_ 9. South China Sea

_5_ 10. Taiwan

Name _____

Chapter Review

Completion

Underline the word or phrase that makes the statement correct.

1. The (<u>Balkans</u>/Netherlands) are located in southeastern Europe.

2. (Alexander I/<u>Mahmud II</u>) was the Ottoman ruler who laid the foundation for a modern Turkey.

3. (The Ottoman Empire/<u>Russia</u>) became the largest state in the world in the eighteenth century.

4. (Hong Xiuquan/<u>Michael Bakunin</u>) became known as the Father of Anarchism.

5. (<u>Alexander II</u>/Nicholas II) abolished serfdom in Russia and freed over twenty million peasants.

6. (<u>Robert Clive</u>/Matthew Perry) defeated Indian forces at the Battle of Plassey.

7. The (<u>Charter</u>/Indies Commerce) Act gave the possessions of the East India Company to the British crown.

8. The British produced (<u>opium</u>/cocaine) from poppy plants in India and exported it to China.

9. The (Song/<u>Qing</u>) dynasty weakened as European nations began dominating Asia.

10. Many Chinese Christians and missionaries suffered during the (<u>Boxer</u>/ Taiping) Rebellion.

11. (Xiuquan/<u>Guangxu</u>) initiated the Hundred Days' Reform in China.

12. (<u>Japan</u>/India) quickly modernized and remained free of European Imperialism.

13. The Meiji Restoration took place in (<u>Japan</u>/India).

14. (<u>Matthew Perry</u>/Leo Tolstoy) pressured Japan to open to trade and end its isolation.

15. The Treaty of (Tokyo/<u>Kanagawa</u>) opened trade between Japan and the rest of the world.

16. The state religion of Japan became (<u>Shintoism</u>/Hinduism).

Matching

Write the correct letter in the blank.

_B_ 17. Chinese ruler

_A_ 18. Expanded Russia's borders

_D_ 19. Came to power in the middle of a Russian revolt

_C_ 20. Russian author

A. ~~Catherine the Great~~
B. ~~Empress Dowager Cixi~~
C. ~~Dostoyevsky~~
D. ~~Nicholas I~~

Name _____

Alvin York and His Struggle with War

Answer the questions at the end based on the following excerpts from Sergeant York's writings.

. . . [A]s long as the records remain I will be officially known as a conscientious objector. I was. I couldn't have been anything else nohow.

At first I [just] couldn't imagine I would have to fight. The war seemed too far away to be mixing me up in it. And I didn't want to be in it nohow. I never had killed nobody, not even in my bad days, and I didn't want to begin now. I turned my back on all of those rowdy things and found a heap of comfort and happiness in religion. I joined the church. It was the Church of Christ in Christian Union. I had [taken] its creed and I had [taken] it without what you might call reservations. I was not a Sunday Christian. I believed in the Bible. And I tried in my own way to live up to it. It was the only creed of my church. To be a member I had to accept the Bible as the inspired word of God. I did. And the Bible said, "Thou shalt not kill." That was so definite a child could understand it. There was no way around or out of it. So you see there were two reasons why I didn't want to go to war. My own experience told me that it weren't right. And the Bible were agin [against] it too.

But Uncle Sam said he wanted me and he wanted me most awful bad. And I had also been brought up to believe in my country. . . . I [kind of] felt that my ancestors would want me to do whatever my country demanded of me.

So you see my religion and my own experience sorter [sort of] told me not to go to war, and the memory of my ancestors [just] as plainly . . . told me to get my gun and go and fight. I didn't know what to do. I am a-telling you there was a war going on inside of me and I didn't know which side to lean on. I was a heap bothered. [It] is a most awful thing when the wishes of your God and your country sorter get mixed up and go against each other. . . .

Pastor Pile was the registrar. He had a store and the post office at Pall Mall, and the Government done instructed him to take the registration for the draft. I went to him and we talked it over, and we read the Bible and prayed together. No matter how we looked at it, we always come up against "Thou shalt not kill." That was the word of God and that was how it was revealed in His Holy Book. There was no [getting] past that nohow. . . .

York applied for an exemption from fighting in the war but was denied. In boot camp, he proved to be an excellent marksman, although he still struggled with the idea of killing others. When York's commander learned of this inner turmoil, he sent York home on leave to resolve the matter.

. . . I went home [from boot camp] and while I was at home we had several services at Greer's [Chapel], and the Lord blessed us and we had a fine meeting. Rev. R. C. Pile and others were helping, and there were a number of people saved during this little meeting. So the Lord was with us. Bless His holy name.

I knowed now that if I went back and told the Major I was still opposed to fighting he would let me out or have me transferred into another branch of the service where I wouldn't have to kill. . . . I talked to Pastor Pile again and again. But all I got from all of this was to get more and more confused. . . . I [just] didn't know what to do; whether to want war or peace; and I didn't know which He wanted me to do.

So I went out on the mountainside and asked Him sorter straight out from the shoulder. I went off to a quiet place not far from my home. I knelt down and I prayed and I prayed all the afternoon, through the night and through part of the next day. I asked Him to have pity on me and show me the light. I begged Him to comfort me if it was His will and tell me what to do. And as I prayed there alone a great peace kinder [kind of] come into my soul and a great calm come over me and I received my assurance. He heard my prayer and He come to me on the mountainside. I didn't see Him, of course, but He was there [just] the same. I knowed He was there. He understood that I didn't want to be a fighter or a killin' man, that I didn't want to go to war and hurt nobody nohow. And yet I wanted to do what my country wanted me to do. I wanted to serve God and my country, too. . . .

So He took pity on me and He gave me the assurance I needed. I didn't understand everything. I didn't understand how He could let me go to war and even kill and yet not hold it agin [against] me. I didn't even want to understand. It was His will and that was enough for me. So at last I begun to see the light. I begun to understand that no matter what a man is forced to do, so long as he is right in his own soul he remains a righteous man. I knowed I would go to war. I knowed I would be protected from all harm, and that so long as I believed in [God] He would not allow even a hair of my head to be harmed.

I arose and thanked Him and went home over the mountains, singing a hymn.

I told my little old mother I was going and not to worry. I was coming back safe and sound. I told my brothers and sisters and I told Pastor Pile.

York, Alvin. *Sergeant York and the Great War: His Own Life Story and War Diary*. Ed. Richard Wheeler. (Rolla, MO: My Father's World, 1998). 67–69, 84–85. Used by permission.

1. Why did Alvin York hesitate to enter the army during World War I? _____

    _____

2. What church did York join? _____

3. Who owned a store and post office in town and served as York's advisor? _____

4. What did York do to determine whether or not he should fight in the war? _____

    _____

5. What was his final decision? With whom did he share this decision? _____

    _____

Name _____

"The Only Thing We Have to Fear . . ."

Answer the questions at the end based on the following excerpts from Franklin D. Roosevelt's speech.

[March 4, 1933]

I am certain that my fellow Americans expect that on my induction into the Presidency I will address them with a candor and a [firmness] which the present situation of our Nation [demands]. This is . . . the time to speak the truth, the whole truth, frankly and boldly. Nor need we shrink from honestly facing conditions in our country today. This great Nation will endure as it has endured, will revive and will prosper. So, first of all, let me assert my firm belief that the only thing we have to fear is fear itself—nameless, unreasoning, unjustified terror which paralyzes needed efforts to convert retreat into advance. In every dark hour of our national life a leadership of frankness and vigor has met with that understanding and support of the people themselves which is essential to victory. I am convinced that you will again give that support to leadership in these critical days.

In such a spirit on my part and on yours we face our common difficulties. They concern . . . only material things. Values have shrunken to fantastic levels; taxes have risen; our ability to pay has fallen; government of all kinds is faced by serious curtailment [shortage] of income; the means of exchange are frozen in the currents of trade; the withered leaves of industrial enterprise lie on every side; farmers find no markets for their produce; the savings of many years in thousands of families are gone.

More important, a host of unemployed citizens face the grim problem of existence, and an equally great number toil with little return. Only a foolish optimist can deny the dark realities of the moment.

Yet our distress comes from no failure of substance. We are stricken by no plague of locusts. Compared with the perils which our forefathers conquered[,] . . . we have still much to be thankful for. Nature still offers her bounty and human efforts have multiplied it. Plenty is at our doorstep, but a generous use of it languishes in the very sight of the supply. Primarily this is because rulers of the exchange of mankind's goods [business leaders] have failed through their own stubbornness and their own incompetence, have admitted their failure, and have abdicated [resigned]. Practices of the unscrupulous [dishonest] money changers [bankers] stand [accused] in the court of public opinion, rejected by the hearts and minds of men.

True they have tried, but their efforts have been cast in the pattern of an outworn tradition. Faced by failure of credit they have proposed only the lending of more money. Stripped of the lure of profit by which to induce our people to follow their false leadership, they have resorted to exhortations, pleading tearfully for restored confidence. They know only the rules of a generation of self-seekers. They have no vision, and when there is no vision the people perish. . . .

Happiness lies not in the mere possession of money; it lies in the joy of achievement, in the thrill of creative effort. The joy and moral stimulation of work no longer must be forgotten in the mad chase of . . . profits. These dark days will be worth all they cost us if they teach us that our true destiny is not to be ministered unto but to minister to ourselves and to our fellow men. . . .

We face the [difficult] days that lie before us in the warm courage of national unity; with the clear consciousness of seeking old and precious moral values; with the clean satisfaction that comes from the stern performance of duty by old and young alike. We aim at the assurance of a rounded and permanent national life.

We do not distrust the future of essential democracy. The people of the United States have not failed. In their need they have registered a mandate that they want direct, vigorous action. They have asked for discipline and direction under leadership. They have made me the present instrument of their wishes. In the spirit of the gift I take it.

In this dedication of a Nation we humbly ask the blessing of God. May He protect each and every one of us. May He guide me in the days to come.

1. What did Roosevelt say America had to fear? _____

2. According to Roosevelt, what group's practices stood judged "in the court of public opinion"?

   _____

3. In what did Roosevelt say happiness lies, rather than in owning money? _____

4. What did the president say was the "true destiny" of Americans? _____

   _____

5. Upon whom did Roosevelt call for blessing, protection, and guidance? _____

Name _____

Chapter Review
Completion

Underline the word or phrase that correctly completes the statement.

1. The Schlieffen Plan called for the German army to first invade (<u>Belgium</u>/Russia).

2. (Stalin/<u>Lenin</u>) signed a treaty with the Germans and took Russia out of World War I.

3. (<u>Total</u>/Offensive) war is a war in which all the resources of a country are devoted to destroying the enemy.

4. The (Bolsheviks/<u>Mensheviks</u>) sought change through peaceful methods.

5. German delegates at (Berlin/<u>Weimar</u>) formed a new government after the war.

6. Benito Mussolini was a (<u>Fascist</u>/Communist) leader in Italy.

7. The Lateran Treaties were agreements between Mussolini and the (Lutheran/<u>Catholic</u>) Church.

8. President (Herbert Hoover/<u>Woodrow Wilson</u>) led in the formation of the League of Nations.

9. The Washington Naval Conference did not prevent (<u>Japan</u>/China) from building more warships.

10. Germany agreed to recognize France's and Belgium's borders in the (Versailles/<u>Locarno</u>) Pact.

11. Those who signed the (<u>Kellogg-Briand</u>/Lateran) Pact agreed to settle their disputes by negotiation rather than by force.

12. (<u>Chiang Kai-shek</u>/Mao Zedong) led the Kuomintang Party after the death of Sun Yat-Sen.

13. During World War I, (Pan-Ottomanism/<u>Pan-Arabism</u>) began to seek a united state that would spread over the Islamic world.

14. Pierre and Marie Curie pioneered work in (electric/<u>radioactive</u>) matter.

15. Post-war literature was largely (<u>despairing</u>/hopeful).

Matching

Write the correct letter in the blank.

_A_ 16. Russia, Serbia, and France

_C_ 17. Controlled United States money supply

_B_ 18. Germany, Austria-Hungary, and the Ottoman Empire

_E_ 19. Trade legislation

_D_ 20. Bismarck's secret agreement with Russia

A. Allies
B. Central Powers
C. Federal Reserve
D. Reinsurance Treaty
E. Smoot-Hawley Tariff Act

Name _____

The Bombing of Rotterdam

Answer the questions at the end based on the following fictionalized account of the bombing of this Dutch city.

May 21, 1947

Although the war has ended and my country is rebuilding, I am still haunted by the memory of the German invasion of our peaceful nation. Our family lived in the beautiful city of Rotterdam in the Netherlands. My father owned a successful manufacturing company, and our family of five (I have two older sisters) lived in a large house overlooking one of the canals that crisscrossed our city. We often enjoyed watching the boats sail up and down the waterways.

In the spring of 1940, I had just turned thirteen and had no idea of the ominous events that were about to turn our lives upside down. We later learned that our leaders knew Germany planned to invade our small country. However, most believed the government's assurances that war could be avoided.

My sisters and I began to suspect that all was not well when Father, after much prayer and seeking of God's will, arranged for us to take an extended trip to the country. Our uncle and his family had a farm a few miles south of our city. Without telling us of the danger he anticipated, Father sent us to visit our relatives on May 1, 1940. He remained in Rotterdam to oversee his business.

I was sure that life on the farm would be boring, and I resented being separated from my friends back in the city. However, within a few days we began to hear troubling reports on the radio of German threats against our land. Then, all of our fears seemed to melt away on May 9 when the prime minister announced that an agreement had been reached with Germany. He assured the Dutch people that their nation would be preserved from war. We went to bed believing that all was well. However, we awoke to the dreadful news that Germany had indeed attacked our country, and we were at war!

Over the next five days, my mother tried to contact my father. We worried as we heard the radio reports of German bombers attacking key targets. Mother feared that Father might be injured or killed if Rotterdam should be bombed.

On May 14 the Germans issued a demand that our country surrender immediately. Otherwise, they would bomb Rotterdam and destroy it! This news sent shivers down my spine, and I worried that my father might be killed. However, our concern soon turned to relief as we heard that the Dutch government had quickly surrendered. Dutch officials believed this would prevent a terrible loss of life and property. Again, we went to bed with some assurance that the worst might be over and that our beloved city would be spared.

Imagine our horror the next morning when we heard that, despite our country's surrender, the German air force had bombed Rotterdam! Over the next several days we learned that the bombing had destroyed the heart of the city. The resulting fires had consumed thousands of buildings and killed hundreds of people. Although it seemed like an eternity, in less than a week we received confirmation that Father had survived the attack and would soon come to stay with us in the country. Even though the assault had destroyed our home, we were thrilled to discover that Father was safe.

Gradually we received news that over eighty thousand people had lost their homes. Where would they live? How would they survive? I wondered. My heart sank as I pondered these troubling questions, but my initial resentment soon turned to gratitude that God had given Father the wisdom to send us out of the city. The farm suddenly seemed a wonderful place to live, now that so many people in our country no longer had a home.

1. In this story, where does the father send his family to protect them? _____

   _____

2. What Dutch city did the Germans bomb on May 14, 1940? _____

3. What action did the Dutch government take on this day, trying to prevent the bombing? _____

   _____

4. What additional damage occurred as a result of the fires following the bombing? _____

   _____

5. How many people lost their homes? _____

6. What fears and questions might have been on the minds of the Dutch people after the German attack?

   _____

   _____

7. How does the narrator's attitude change by the end of the story? _____

   _____

Name _____

Churchill's Inspiring Words

Answer the questions below based on the following excerpts from Winston Churchill's writings.

[June 4, 1940]

. . . I have, myself, full confidence that if all do their duty . . . we shall prove ourselves once again able to defend our Island home, to ride out the storm of war, and to outlive the menace of tyranny, if necessary for years, if necessary alone.

(https://en.wikisource.org/wiki/We_shall_fight_on_the_beaches)

1. What did Churchill believe would be the ultimate outcome of World War II?

   _____ to ride out the storm of war _____

2. For how long and under what circumstances did Churchill believe his country would fight to defend itself?

   _____ for years alone _____

[June 18, 1940]

. . . [T]he Battle of France is over. I expect that the Battle of Britain is about to begin. Upon this battle depends the survival of . . . our own British life, and the long continuity of our institutions and our Empire. The whole fury and might of the enemy must very soon be turned on us. Hitler knows that he will have to break us in this Island or lose the war. If we can stand up to him, all Europe may be free and the life of the world may move forward into broad, sunlit uplands. But if we fail, then the whole world . . . will sink into the abyss of a new Dark Age. . . . Let us therefore brace ourselves to our duties, and so bear ourselves that, if the British Empire and its Commonwealth last for a thousand years, men will still say, "*This* was their finest hour."

(https://en.wikisource.org/wiki/Their_Finest_Hour)

3. According to Churchill, which country would stand up to Hitler, allowing all of Europe to regain its freedom? _____ Britain _____

4. In the event that Germany defeated the British, what might happen to the world? _____

   _____

5. What did Churchill hope future generations would say about the British living during World War II?

   _____

Name _____

The Iron Curtain

Answer the questions at the end based on the following excerpts from Winston Churchill's speech at Westminster College in Fulton, Missouri.

[March 5, 1946]

Beware, I say; time may be short. . . . A shadow has fallen upon the scenes so lately lighted by the Allied victory. Nobody knows what Soviet Russia and its Communist international [organization] intends to do in the immediate future, or what are the limits, if any, to their expansive and proselytizing tendencies. . . . From Stettin in the Baltic to Trieste in the Adriatic an iron curtain has descended across the Continent. Warsaw, Berlin, Prague, Vienna, Budapest, Belgrade, Bucharest and Sofia, all these famous cities . . . lie in what I must call the Soviet sphere, and all are subject in one form or another, not only to Soviet influence but to a very high and, in many cases, increasing measure of control from Moscow. . . . [I]n a great number of countries, far from the Russian frontiers and throughout the world, Communist fifth columns are established and work in complete unity and absolute obedience to the directions they receive from the Communist center. Except in the British Commonwealth and in the United States where Communism is in its infancy, the Communist parties or fifth columns constitute a growing challenge and peril to Christian [civilization]. These are somber facts . . . but we should be most unwise not to face them squarely while time remains.

Winston Churchill. *Never Give In: The Best of Winston Churchill's Speeches*. Ed. Winston S. Churchill (New York: Hyperion, 2003). 414, 420.

1 According to Churchill, what had descended across the European continent? _____

2. What city did Churchill mention as controlling many other cities? _____

3. According to Churchill, what was a threat to many countries? _____

4. According to Churchill, what two nations did not face this threat? _____

_____

5. What did Churchill propose to do about this threat? _____

Name _____

The World at War

Write the correct letter in the blank.

A. Allies	E. Luftwaffe	I. Operation T-4	M. Shoah
B. appeasement	F. May 8, 1945	J. Pact of Steel	N. Sudetenland
C. existentialism	G. Midway Island	K. Rome-Berlin Axis	O. Third Reich
D. Holocaust	H. Munich Conference	L. September 2, 1945	

_D_ 1. Nazi program that killed many Jews

_H_ 2. European leaders meeting prior to World War II

_O_ 3. The German empire under Hitler

_N_ 4. Area of Czechoslovakia that the Germans conquered

_E_ 5. German air force

_L_ 6. V-J Day (victory in Japan)

_K_ 7. 1936 alliance between Mussolini and Hitler

_J_ 8. 1939 military alliance between Mussolini and Hitler

_M_ 9. The Jewish name for the Holocaust

_I_ 10. Nazis' program of "mercy killing"

_C_ 11. Philosophy encouraging free choice and accepting consequences

_B_ 12. Avoiding conflict by making concessions

_G_ 13. location of an important American naval base

_F_ 14. V-E Day (victory in Europe)

_A_ 15. Declared war when Hitler invaded Poland

Name _____

Chapter Review

Completion

Underline the word or phrase that correctly completes the statement.

1. (Franco/Mussolini) was a Fascist dictator in Spain.

2. Hirohito was a Japanese (emperor/military general) during World War II.

3. Mussolini sent Italy's modern army into (Egypt/Ethiopia) and quickly conquered this African country.

4. The (Anti-Comintern/Berlin Axis) Pact allied Germany and Japan against Communist Russia.

5. Nearly two million Germans invaded Poland on (May 8, 1945/September 1, 1939).

6. The Japanese attacked America's naval base at Pearl Harbor on (June 22, 1941/December 7, 1941).

7. General Bernard L. Montgomery defeated German forces in (Britain/Africa).

8. General Erwin Rommel fought in (Russia/North Africa).

9. (Douglas MacArthur/Dwight D. Eisenhower) became the supreme Allied commander in the Pacific.

10. June 6, 1944, is often referred to as (D-day/V-E Day).

11. Hitler tried to break through the Allied line at the Battle of the (Midway/Bulge).

12. President Truman ordered atomic bombs to be dropped on Hiroshima and (Nagasaki/Tokyo).

13. The Soviet Union seized most of (China/Eastern Europe) after the war.

14. Political rivalry that stops short of actual war is called a (total/cold) war.

15. Jackson Pollock developed a form of painting called (abstract expressionism/existentialism).

Matching

Write the correct letter in the blank.

_B_ 16. United States general

_C_ 17. German ruler

_E_ 18. Japanese general

_A_ 19. English prime minister

_D_ 20. German general

A. Neville Chamberlain
B. Dwight D. Eisenhower
C. Adolf Hitler
D. Erwin Rommel
E. Tojo

Name _____

China and Taiwan

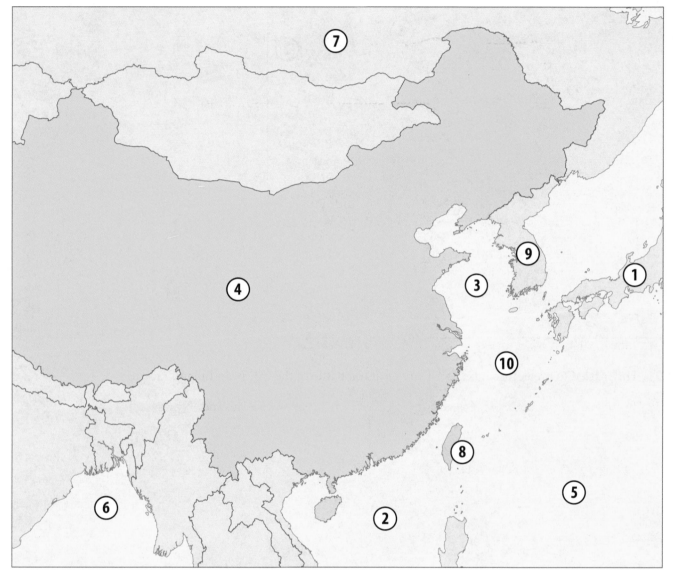

Locate the following on the map and write the number in the blank beside the term.

_6_ 1. Bay of Bengal

_4_ 2. China

_10_ 3. East China Sea

_1_ 4. Japan

_9_ 5. Korea

_5_ 6. Pacific Ocean

_2_ 7. South China Sea

_7_ 8. Soviet Union

_8_ 9. Taiwan

_3_ 10. Yellow Sea

Name _____

Korean War

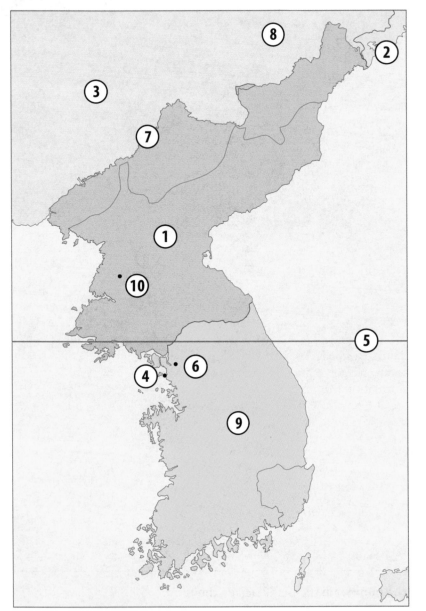

Locate the following on the map and write the number in the blank beside the term.

_3_ 1. China

_4_ 2. Inchon

_8_ 3. Manchuria

_1_ 4. North Korea

_10_ 5. Pyongyang

_6_ 6. Seoul

_9_ 7. South Korea

_5_ 8. 38th Parallel

_2_ 9. USSR

_7_ 10. Yalu River

Children of the Storm

Answer the questions below based on the following excerpt from Natasha Vins's work.

. . . A friend from Moscow had brought the news that Papa had been arrested two days earlier. Even though he had already been in hiding for three years and we had known that he could be arrested at any moment [for being a Christian leader], this news was sudden and brought a stab of pain. . . .

The next day, our Sunday worship service in the forest was brutally disrupted. Policemen beat the men and twisted their arms. They pushed around women and children. With my own eyes, I saw seventy-five-year[-]old Fanya Andreevna get shoved so hard that her cane went flying to the side and she fell down. I ran to help her get up, but she could not because she was badly injured. Many believers were arrested that day and sentenced to fifteen days in jail.

At our home the police conducted another house search. They officially informed us that Papa had been arrested and that while his case was being prepared for trial he would be held in Lefortovo Prison in Moscow. The prosecutor in Moscow assigned an investigator in Kiev to question family members.

One day at [my brother] Peter's school his third-grade teacher was told to send him to the principal's office. Peter figured out that he was going to be interrogated. So instead of going to the principal's office, he ran out of school, got on a bus, and went to the home of relatives who lived across town. Mama happened to be there and decided not to bring Peter home, but to send him to a village to stay with a Christian family in order to protect him from interrogation.

I did not succeed in evading interrogation. When the investigator came to my school, the teacher personally took me to the principal's office. The investigator started to question me about Papa, but I refused to answer his questions. He got angry and shouted at me as did the principal, but they were unable to get any information from me. . . .

[Several months later,] we went to see Papa at Lefortovo Prison. All five of us—Mama, Babushka, Peter, Lisa, and I—were allowed in. At the prison entrance the guards checked our passports and birth certificates. Mama showed the notice from the judge allowing us a visit. All the documents were in order so we were permitted to enter.

A guard led us into a large room that had no other furniture except for a table and several chairs. He ordered us to sit on one side of the table. The chair reserved for Papa was on the opposite side. . . . [W]e were allowed a thirty-minute visit. . . . As we said our last good-byes, the guard entered, announcing, "It's over. Time to leave!"

We left the prison gates and walked to the bus stop through the snowy streets of Moscow. The day was December 2, 1966. We had to get to the train station and return home to Kiev. There was nothing left to be done that would keep us in Moscow. As for Papa, he would soon be on his way to a prison camp in the Ural Mountains.

Children of the Storm: The Autobiography of Natasha Vins translated by Jane Vins Comden. Copyright 2002 BJU Press. All rights reserved. 21–24.

1. Why was Natasha's father arrested? _____

2. Where were the believers holding their worship service? _____

3. How did the police treat the women and children? _____

4. What did Natasha learn about her father when authorities searched her house? _____
   _____

5. Why did Peter leave the school and go to the home of relatives? _____
   _____

6. When Natasha refused to provide the investigator and the principal with information about her father, how did they respond? _____

7. Where was Natasha's father to be sent? _____

"Tear Down This Wall!"

Answer the questions at the end based on the following excerpts from President Reagan's speech.

[June 12, 1987]

Twenty-four years ago, President John F. Kennedy visited Berlin, speaking to the people of this city and the world at the City Hall. Well, since then two other presidents have come, each in his turn, to Berlin. And today I, myself, make my second visit to your city. We come to Berlin, we American presidents, because it's our duty to speak, in this place, of freedom. But I must confess, we're drawn here by other things as well: by the feeling of history in this city, more than 500 years older than our own nation; by the beauty of the Grunewald and the Tiergarten; most of all, by your courage and determination. Perhaps the composer Paul Lincke understood something about American presidents. You see, like so many presidents before me, I come here today because wherever I go, whatever I do: Ich hab noch einen Koffer in Berlin. [I still have a suitcase in Berlin.] Our gathering today is being broadcast throughout Western Europe and North America. I understand that it is being seen and heard as well in the East. To those listening throughout Eastern Europe, a special word: Although I cannot be with you, I address my remarks to you just as surely as to those standing here before me. For I join you, as I join your fellow countrymen in the West, in this firm, this unalterable belief: Es gibt nur ein Berlin. [There is only one Berlin.]

Behind me stands a wall that encircles the free sectors of this city, part of a vast system of barriers that divides the entire continent of Europe. From the Baltic, south, those barriers cut across Germany in a gash of barbed wire, concrete, dog runs, and guard towers. Farther south, there may be no visible, no obvious wall. But there remain armed guards and checkpoints all the same—still a restriction on the right to travel, still an instrument to impose upon ordinary men and women the will of a totalitarian state. Yet it is here in Berlin where the wall emerges most clearly; here, cutting across your city, where the news photo and the television screen have imprinted this brutal division of a continent upon the mind of the world. Standing before the Brandenburg Gate, every man is a German, separated from his fellow men. Every man is a Berliner, forced to look upon a scar. President von Weizsacker has said, "The German question is open as long as the Brandenburg Gate is closed." Today I say: As long as the gate is closed, as long as this scar of a wall is permitted to stand, it is not the German question alone that remains open, but the question of freedom for all mankind. Yet I do not come here to lament. For I find in Berlin a message of hope, even in the shadow of this wall, a message of triumph. . . .

And now the Soviets themselves may, in a limited way, be coming to understand the importance of freedom. We hear much from Moscow about a new policy of reform and openness. Some political prisoners have been released. Certain foreign news broadcasts are no longer being jammed. Some economic enterprises have been permitted to operate with greater freedom from state control. Are these the beginnings of profound changes in the Soviet state? Or are they token gestures, intended to raise false hopes in the West, or to strengthen the Soviet system without changing it? We welcome change and openness; for we believe that freedom and security go together, that the advance of human liberty can only strengthen the cause of world peace. There is one sign the Soviets can make that would be unmistakable, that would advance dramatically the cause of freedom and peace.

General Secretary Gorbachev, if you seek peace, if you seek prosperity for the Soviet Union and Eastern Europe, if you seek liberalization: Come here to this gate! Mr. Gorbachev, open this gate! **Mr. Gorbachev, tear down this wall!** . . .

And I invite Mr. Gorbachev: Let us work to bring the Eastern and Western parts of the city closer together, so that all the inhabitants of all Berlin can enjoy the benefits that come with life in one of the great cities of the world. To open Berlin still further to all Europe, East and West, let us expand the vital air access to this city, finding ways of making commercial air service to Berlin more convenient, more comfortable, and more economical. We look to the day when West Berlin can become one of the chief aviation hubs in all central Europe. . . .

. . . Yes, across Europe, this wall will fall. For it cannot withstand faith; it cannot withstand truth. The wall cannot withstand freedom. . . .

http://en.wikisource.org/wiki/Ronald_Reagan%27s_Berlin_Wall_Speech

1. What American president had visited Berlin and made a famous speech twenty-four years before President Reagan's speech? _____

2. How many years older is the city of Berlin than the United States? _____

3. By what historic gate did Reagan give this speech? _____

4. Who was the General Secretary of the Soviet Union during this period? _____

5. What does President Reagan challenge the Soviet leader to do in order to seek peace and prosperity for the Soviet Union? _____

Name _____

Chapter Review

Completion

Underline the word or phrase that correctly completes the statement.

1. Konrad Adenauer quickly improved the economy of (France/<u>Germany</u>) with a free market.

2. The (MacArthur/<u>Marshall</u>) Plan helped western European nations recover from World War II.

3. (Communism/<u>Democracy</u>) stresses the individual's role in government and allows the operation of privately owned businesses.

4. Chiang Kai-shek founded the Republic of China in (Beijing/Taiwan).

5. The (Great Leap Forward/Cultural Revolution) failed and caused famine in China.

6. UN forces fought the North (Koreans/Vietnamese) at Inchon.

7. Ho Chi Minh declared Vietnam independent from (England/France).

8. Sputnik was the first man-made (satellite/space defense weapon).

9. Mohandas Gandhi used (anarchy/passive resistance) to achieve Indian independence from Britain.

10. The British partitioned the sub-continent of India into India and (Afghanistan/Pakistan).

11. The (Tel Aviv/Balfour) Declaration acknowledged Israel's need for a homeland.

12. The (Six-Day/Cold) War resulted from an Arab attempt to invade Israel.

13. The Soviets invaded Czechoslovakia in 1968 because its leader (Wałęsa/Dubček) was restoring rights to the Czechs.

14. The (Chinese/Soviets) invaded Afghanistan in 1979 but could not conquer the country.

15. The Solidarity movement in Poland became an (anti-American/anti-Communist) effort to oppose Soviet domination.

Matching

Write the correct letter in the blank.

_C_ 16. Leader of the Soviet Union after Stalin's death

_____ 17. Communist leader in Vietnam

_____ 18. President of France

_____ 19. Fortieth president of the United States

_____ 20. Led the Conservative Party in Great Britain to victory

A. Charles de Gaulle
B. Ho Chi Minh
C. Nikita Krushchev
D. Ronald Reagan
E. Margaret Thatcher

Name _____

European Union

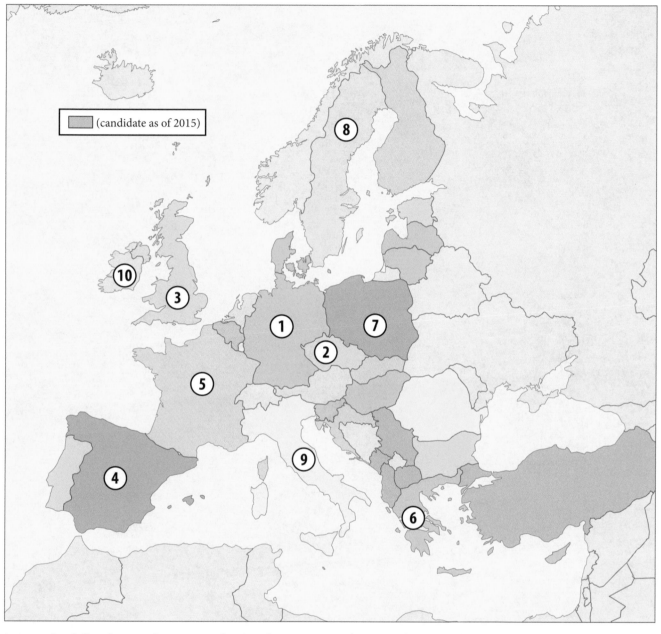

(candidate as of 2015)

Locate the following on the map and write the corresponding number in each blank.

_____ 1. Czech Republic

_____ 2. France

_____ 3. Germany

_____ 4. Greece

_____ 5. Ireland

_____ 6. Italy

_____ 7. Poland

_____ 8. Spain

_____ 9. Sweden

_____ 10. United Kingdom

Name _____

Stem Cell Research

Answer the questions at the end based on the following excerpts from the fourth edition of *BIOLOGY*.

Stem cell technology holds much promise in the treatment of disease and the repair of injuries. But what exactly are stem cells, and where do they come from? Stem cells are cells that have the ability to divide almost indefinitely and to give rise to, or [modify] into, specialized cells. For example, a stem cell in the tip of a plant root can become any of the types of cells found in plants. Due to environmental and hormonal cues, the cell develops into a particular type of cell; it becomes [modified] or specialized. Similarly, animal embryos contain stem cells that [modify] to become the various tissues and organs of the animal. The same is true for human embryos. Since much of the controversy regarding stem cells relates to using human stem cells, that context is used in this section. . . .

When a sperm cell fertilizes an ovum, a zygote is formed. That one cell has the potential to give rise to all of the cell types in the human body. . . . When the zygote divides into two cells, each of these cells can also become any of the cell types in the body. If these two cells should separate and continue to grow separately, they would form identical twins.

As the zygote continues to grow by cell division, the cells begin to [modify] into the parts of the early embryo. They can give rise to many, but not all, cell types. . . . In other words, these cells have lost some of their potential to specialize. As these . . . cells continue to divide, they form stem cells that will give rise to particular tissues such as blood and skin. Now they are committed to a specific type of tissue but still are not fully specialized. For example, bone marrow stem cells can still give rise to all of the various types of human blood cells. . . .

The larger controversy over stem cells is not whether scientists should be performing stem cell research but rather concerns the source of the stem cells used in research. There are two basic sources for stem cells—embryonic and adult.

As the name states, human embryonic stem cells . . . come from human embryos. In order to obtain embryonic stem cells, the embryo is destroyed. Since life begins at conception[,] . . . human lives are [taken] in order to harvest embryonic stem cells for research (Ps. 51:5; 139:13–16). . . .

. . . Bone marrow stem cells have been successfully used for more than thirty years in the treatment of leukemia. More recently, scientists have isolated [adult] stem cells in a variety of tissues, such as nerves, skin, and blood vessels. Although [adult stem cells] are more specialized than embryonic stem cells, researchers are finding that [adult] stem cells can be made to [modify] into many types of tissue cells. . . .

Scientists are looking to stem cells for new treatments and cures for many diseases and disorders. For example, in insulin-dependent diabetes, researchers theorize that if stem cells can be harvested, [modified] into the proper kind of pancreatic cells, and then transplanted into the diabetic's pancreas, the newly [modified] cells will continue to grow and produce insulin. If [this procedure is] successful, the person would no longer need to inject insulin to treat his diabetes. Many other conditions are being studied to determine whether they can be successfully treated with stem cells.

At this time, only [adult] stem cells have been used to successfully treat human diseases. In fact, [adult] stem cells are already being used to treat over 70 different diseases, including diabetes, Parkinson disease, and several forms of cancer. Recent studies continue to find that [adult] stem cells can be [modified] into many cell types and have some advantages over embryonic stem cells. [Adult] stem cells are easier to grow and to [modify] into specific cell types. . . .

. . . The most important advantage of [adult] stem cells is that no embryo is killed to harvest the cells. If researchers should ever determine that embryonic stem cells are superior to [adult] stem cells, would that justify their use? Those who support embryonic stem cell research argue that it is acceptable to sacrifice human embryos to advance scientific and medical knowledge for the benefit of all humanity. They refuse to accept that human embryos are human beings from the moment of conception, created in the image of God.

The use of the knowledge that God has allowed man to discover must always be guided by scriptural principles. The Bible states that killing an innocent person is never justified (Gen. 9:6). Doing evil so that some good might result is also condemned (Rom. 3:8). Therefore, even if all of humanity's suffering could be relieved, Christians must stand against all research and treatments that are in opposition to scriptural principles.

Brad R. Batdorf and Elizabeth Lacy. *Biology*. 4th ed. (Greenville, SC: BJU Press, 2011). 158–61.

1. What are stem cells? _____

_____

2–3. What are the two basic sources for stem cells? _____

4. Which of the two types requires the destruction of a human life in order to obtain the stem cells?

_____

5. Which of the two types of stem cells has been used successfully to treat human diseases? _____

6. Is killing an innocent person ever justifiable? _____

Name _____

Crossword Puzzle

Across

2. Common currency of the European Union
5. Using these in medical research does not present a moral dilemma
8. Latest form of Islamic extremism
10. Movement that gained control of Saudi Arabia and teaches a new interpretation of Islam
12. Terrorist network based in Afghanistan
13. The regions of Latin America, India, China, and Africa
14. A persecuted Chinese Christian

Down

1. Economic and political alliance of nearly 30 European nations
2. Using these in medical research presents a moral dilemma
3. Saudi extremist that built a terrorist network
4. Enables states to trade with one another without restriction
6. Dictator of Iraq
7. Common currency used by the West African Economic and Monetary Union
9. Muslim religious schools
11. A radical Muslim group

Name _____

Chapter Review

Underline the word or phrase that correctly completes the statement.

1. Many people who insist that man is causing climate change and that dire consequences are just over the horizon demand (solutions/consensus) from scientists.

2. The European Union is an economic and political alliance of nearly (twenty/thirty) nations.

3. Conflict between El Salvador and (Nicaragua/Honduras) has posed a threat to the Central American Common Market.

4. No technological development has had more impact on daily living than the (Internet/radio).

5. (Embryonic/Adult) stem cell research does not pose a moral dilemma.

6. The Twin Towers and the (Capitol/Pentagon) were attacked on September 11, 2001.

7. (Osama bin Laden/Saddam Hussein) became the dictator of Iraq.

8. Afghanistan came under the control of a radical Muslim group called the (Madrassas/Taliban).

9. Wang Mingdao was a Christian leader in (China/India).

10. The (Taliban/Wahhabists) gained control of Saudi Arabia and have spread the literal application of Islam to other countries.

11. Biblical Christianity is spreading rapidly in regions known as the global (south/west).

12. Iran and (India/Afghanistan) are nations that support terrorism.

13. (Saudi Arabia/Iraq) invaded Kuwait in 1990 and seized its oil reserves.

14. Eight West African states currently form a union to promote (military/economic) cooperation.

15. Trade provides an opportunity for Christians to evangelize, helping them to fulfill the (Creation Mandate/Great Commission).

Matching

Write the correct letter in the blank.

_____ 16. Enables states to trade with one another without restriction

_____ 17. Common currency of the European Union

_____ 18. Trade areas without quota and tariff restrictions

_____ 19. Common currency of West Africa

_____ 20. West African organization that promotes economic cooperation

A. CFA franc
B. Economic and Monetary Union
C. euro
D. free trade areas
E. single market